# Language Arts Handbook
## Grade Four
## Table of Contents

# Language Arts Handbook
## Grade Four
## Introduction

This book is designed to help review and reinforce the language skills that students will master in the fourth grade. It is a comprehensive handbook that addresses a broad range of the language concepts that students will encounter at this grade level. It can be used effectively as a tool to reinforce language skills at school or at home, or to keep skills sharp over extended vacations.

### Organization

These activities are designed to reinforce the language skills that are important for students in the fourth grade. This book is divided into eight units: Grammar, Sentences, Vocabulary and Usage, Capitalization and Punctuation, Kinds of Writing, Paragraphs, Resource Materials and Research, and Reading Comprehension. Each section focuses on one or two related concepts, and review pages appear at the beginning of each unit to give teachers or parents the opportunity to gauge understanding and to signal if more practice is needed.

- **Grammar.** Several major parts of speech — nouns, verbs, adjectives, adverbs, pronouns, compound words, and contractions — are defined, and students are given the opportunity for practice.

- **Sentences.** Students learn the parts of a sentence, the different kinds of sentences, how to join sentences, and how to write clear, effective sentences.

- **Vocabulary and Usage.** Students review synonyms, antonyms, prefixes, suffixes, homographs, homophones, abbreviations, and subject-verb agreement, and study common spelling problems.

- **Capitalization and Punctuation.** Students study the common uses of capitalization, such as the beginning of sentences, names of people, places, days, months, and titles. Students practice correct usage of the period, the question mark, the exclamation point, the comma, the colon, the apostrophe, underlines, and quotation marks.

- **Kinds of Writing.** Several common types of writing are reviewed, including story and story dialogue, poem, play, news story, magazine article, autobiography, friendly letter, invitation, thank-you note, envelope address, journal entry, and book report.

- **Paragraphs.** Paragraphs are defined and good paragraph writing is explained. Students examine the different types of paragraphs, including how-to, comparison, contrast, cause-and-effect, definition, descriptive, opinion, and persuasive, and work with each type.

- **Resource Materials and Research.** Students review the parts of a book, dictionary, encyclopedia, and atlas skills. Fiction and nonfiction writing is addressed. Students learn how to read for information, take notes, make outlines, write rough drafts, and complete research reports.

- **Reading Comprehension.** Important comprehension skills are practiced, including drawing conclusions, comparing, contrasting, classifying, identifying details, sequencing, cause and effect, judgments, summarizing, predicting outcomes, main idea, paraphrasing, distinguishing between reality and fantasy, and identifying problems and solutions.

## Use
This book is designed for independent use by students who have been introduced to the skills and concepts described. Copies of the activities can be given to individuals, pairs of students, or small groups for completion. They may be used as a center activity. If students are familiar with the content, the worksheets may also be used as homework.

To begin, determine the implementation that fits your students' needs and your classroom structure. The following plan suggests a format for this implementation.

1. **Explain** the purpose of the worksheets to your students. Let them know that these activities will be fun as well as helpful.

2. **Review** the mechanics of how you want the students to work with the activities. Do you want them to work in groups? Are the activities for homework?

3. **Decide** how you would like to use the assessments. They can be given before and after a unit to determine progress, or only after a unit to assess how well the concepts are learned. Determine whether you will send the tests home or keep them in the students' portfolios.

4. **Introduce** students to the process and the purpose of the activities. Go over the directions. Work with children when they have difficulty. Work only a few pages at a time to avoid pressure.

5. **Do** a practice activity together.

## Additional Notes
- **Parent Communication.** Send the Letter to Parents home with students so that parents will know what to expect and how they can best help their child.

- **Bulletin Board.** Display completed work to show student progress.

- **Assessments.** The first page of each unit is a unit assessment. You can use the tests as diagnostic tools by administering them before children begin the activities. After children have completed each unit, let them retake the unit test to see the progress they have made. The assessments may be sent home or kept in portfolios for parent/teacher conferencing.

- **Center Activities.** Use the worksheets as a center activity to give students the opportunity to work cooperatively.

- **Have fun.** Working with these activities can be fun as well as meaningful for you and your students.

**Dear Parent,**

During this school year, our class will be using an activity book to reinforce the language skills that we are learning. By working together, we can be sure that your child not only masters these language skills but also becomes confident in his or her abilities.

From time to time, I may send home activity sheets. To help your child, please consider the following suggestions:

• Provide a quiet place to work.
• Go over the directions together.
• Encourage your child to do his or her best.
• Check the lesson when it is complete.
• Note improvements as well as problems.

Help your child maintain a positive attitude about the activities. Let your child know that each lesson provides an opportunity to have fun and to learn. Above all, enjoy this time you spend with your child. As your child's language skills develop, he or she will feel your support.

Thank you for your help.

**Cordially,**

Name _____ Date _____

Choose one of the terms from the box to name each of the underlined words.

| | | | |
|---|---|---|---|
| common noun | proper noun | plural noun | possessive noun |
| present tense verb | past tense verb | adjective | pronoun |
| compound word | contraction | | |

1. <u>Eskimos</u> live in the coldest places in the world. _____

2. Paula loved her new <u>jacket</u>. _____

3. <u>They</u> are the dogs that pull sleds. _____

4. Aunt Sabra is my <u>favorite</u> aunt. _____

5. The corn is <u>growing</u> very tall. _____

6. My <u>father's</u> car is in the parking lot. _____

7. <u>That's</u> not the way he usually parks. _____

8. Did you find your <u>baseball</u> yet? _____

9. There are so many <u>sauces</u> from which to choose! _____

10. We <u>went</u> to the movies last night. _____

Circle the <u>linking verb</u> or the <u>helping verb</u> in each sentence.

11. Sometimes the wind is dangerous.

12. The clouds will release the rain soon.

Write the past tense of each verb.

13. come _____     18. say _____

14. go _____     19. take _____

15. eat _____     20. grow _____

16. begin _____     21. find _____

17. think _____     22. become _____

Name _____ Date _____

## Naming Nouns

☞ A **noun** is a word that names a person, place, or thing.

☞ A **common noun** names any person, place, or thing. It is a general word that begins with a small letter.

birthday    girl    parka

☞ A **proper noun** names a particular person, place, or thing. A proper noun begins with a capital letter.

Antarctica    Eeka    Mount McKinley

✏ **Practice**

Read each sentence. Find the nouns. Underline each *common noun* once. Underline each *proper noun* twice.

1. Eskimos live in the coldest places in the world.

2. Many of them live in Alaska, the largest state in the United States.

3. Other communities are found in Greenland and Canada.

4. These people have adjusted to very bitter temperatures.

5. Eskimos who live in the Arctic hunt polar bears.

6. The hunters also track walruses.

7. These animals are valuable for their meat and for their tusks of ivory.

8. This hard material is used to make knives, hooks, and other tools.

9. For centuries Eskimos have used ice from the sea for their fresh drinking water.

10. They speak a language that is different from the speech of other

    American Indians.

11. Many Eskimos once lived in special homes.

12. These buildings are called igloos.

Name _____  Date _____

## Good Form

☞ A **singular noun** names one person, place, or thing.

girl    school    book

☞ A **plural noun** names more than one person, place, or thing.

storm—storms        room—rooms
basket—baskets      sled—sleds
day—days            nose—noses
baby—babies         body—bodies
fox—foxes           dish—dishes

✏ **Practice**

Read each sentence. Choose and circle the singular or plural form of each noun in ( ).

1. The teacher told all the (student, students) that school was closing early.

2. She asked the fifth (grader, graders) to help.

3. The older students were asked to walk all of the young (one, ones) home.

4. Paula wanted this to be her best (birthday, birthdays) yet.

5. A new (puppy, puppies) greeted Paula when she got home.

6. Many (guest, guests) came to Paula's party.

7. Paula received a beautiful new (scarf, scarves) from her sister.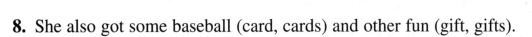

8. She also got some baseball (card, cards) and other fun (gift, gifts).

9. The most wonderful gift of all was a new (bedspread, bedspreads) and

   curtains for her room.

10. Paula's mother would hang the (curtain, curtains) in her windows.

Name _____ Date _____

## More Than One

☞ To form the plural of most nouns, add *s*.
   seal—seals          fur—furs

☞ To form the plural of nouns that end with *s, ch, sh, x,* or *z,* add *es*.
   porch—porches     wish—wishes          fox—foxes

☞ To form the plural of a noun that ends in *y* with a consonant before it, change the *y* to *i* and add *es*.
   story—stories        party—parties

☞ To form the plural of a noun that ends in *y* with a vowel before it, add *s*.
   key—keys              birthday—birthdays

☞ To form the plural of most nouns that end in *f* or *fe,* change the *f* to *v* and add *es*.
   scarf—scarves        knife—knives

☞ Some nouns do not add *s* or *es* to make their plural forms.
   foot—feet              child—children          man—men

☞ A few nouns are the same in both the singular and plural form.
   reindeer—reindeer   caribou—caribou       moose—moose

## ✐ Practice

Read each sentence. Write the plural form of the noun in ( ).

1. Dogs that pull sleds are called _____. (husky)

2. They are about two _____ tall. (foot)

3. Eskimos may use _____ to chop ice. (ax)

4. People in cold climates lead hard _____. (life)

5. _____ live in the Arctic. (walrus)

6. Many _____ and _____ live there, too. (caribou, reindeer)

7. Eskimos used ivory to make _____. (tool)

8. Some Eskimo _____ weave baskets. (woman)

Name _____  Date _____

☞ A **possessive noun** shows ownership.

      The <u>home of her cousin</u> was next door.

      Her <u>cousin's</u> home was next door.

☞ Add an **apostrophe** (') and *s* to singular nouns to show possession.

      Today is <u>Dana's</u> birthday.

      Her <u>father's</u> traps were covered with snow.

☞ Add an apostrophe to plural nouns that end in *s* to show possession.

      The <u>Eskimos'</u> way of life has changed.

      The <u>girls'</u> boots crunched through the snow.

✐ **Practice**

Rewrite each sentence, changing the underlined words. Use a singular or plural possessive noun in each sentence.

1. Mary loved listening to <u>the stories of her grandfather</u>.

_____

2. Mary and her mother saw <u>the snow machines of their neighbors</u>.

_____

3. All the <u>friends of the family</u> came to the birthday party.

_____

4. Mary opened the <u>presents of the relatives</u>.

_____

5. She read her birthday cards, and some of the <u>messages of the cards</u> were funny.

_____

6. <u>The present of James</u> was a surprise.

_____

7. The <u>heart of Mary</u> was full of love.

_____

Name _____ Date _____

## Comparing and Contrasting, p. 2

☞ Form the possessive of a singular noun by adding an apostrophe (') and *s*.

      catcher—catcher's   boy—boy's

☞ Form the possessive of a plural noun that ends in *s* by adding an apostrophe only. Otherwise, add an apostrophe and *s*.

      friends—friends'    men—men's

### ✎ Practice

Read each sentence. Change the underlined noun in each sentence to the correct possessive form. Write the new word on the line.

1. Dan was saving for his brother <u>Mike</u> birthday gift. _____

2. The newspaper ad said the <u>car</u> price was seventy dollars. _____

3. <u>Dan</u> mouth fell open. How could a remote-controlled car cost so much?

    _____

4. His <u>dad</u> advice was to do some odd jobs._____

5. Dan knocked on all his <u>neighbors</u> doors. _____

6. He had to find out about <u>people</u> needs. _____

7. A woman wanted Dan to clean her <u>pet</u> house. _____

8. One man hired Dan to do tricks at a <u>children</u> party.

    _____

9. With his <u>neighbors</u> help, Dan had earned the money. _____

10. He rushed downtown before the department <u>store</u> closing time of 5 P.M.

    _____

11. Dan's <u>brother</u> smile was wide when he saw the car. _____

Name _____ Date _____

## Get Into Action!

☞ An **action verb** is a word that shows an action. An action verb is often the key word in the predicate. It tells what the subject does.

        The children <u>tricked</u> their father.
        They <u>played</u> a practical joke on him.

### ✏ Practice

Complete each sentence with an action verb from the box.

| | | |
|---|---|---|
| talked | surprised | knocked |
| flashed | laughed | climbed |
| added | propped | yelled |
| stuffed | carved | shivered |

1. The children _____ a scary head out of a pumpkin.

2. They _____ up to the hayloft.

3. Then they _____ about what they would do.

4. The children _____ from the cold and excitement.

5. They _____ the clothes full of hay.

6. Then they _____ the head of the pumpkin to the body.

7. Finally, they _____ their creation in the loft doorway.

8. The children _____ a light on their ghost.

9. Their father was _____ to see the man in the loft.

10. One of the children _____ the man out of the loft.

11. Their father _____ when the man fell.

12. The children and their father _____ at the joke.

**Verbs**
**Unit One: Grammar**
Language Arts 4, SV 3890-5

Name _____ Date _____

## Now and Then

☞ The time expressed by a verb is called the **tense**.

☞ **Present tense** shows action that happens now or regularly. Most present tense verbs that follow singular subjects end in *s* or *es*.

> The boy <u>pushes</u> the door open.
> Each child <u>climbs</u> to the hayloft.

☞ Present tense verbs that follow plural subjects do not take an *s* or *es* ending.

> The children <u>plan</u> their trick carefully.

☞ **Past tense** shows action that happened in the past. To form the past tense of many verbs, add *ed*.

> The children <u>worked</u> on their plan.

☞ **Future tense** shows action that will happen in the future. Verbs that tell about the future have the helping verb *will*.

> They <u>will give</u> their father the scare of his life.

## ✐ Practice

Read each sentence. Write the correct form of the verb in ( ).

1. Do you think the trick _____? (work—future)

2. The children certainly _____ so. (hope—present)

3. Their idea _____ lots of planning. (need—past)

4. A branch _____ against the house. (bang—past)

5. The children _____ great practical jokes! (play—present)

Name _____ Date _____

## A Parade of Verbs

☞ To form the past tense of many action verbs, add *ed*.

watch–watched　　　　　　start–started

☞ To add *ed* to action verbs that end with *e*, drop the *e* and add *ed*.

live–lived　　dance–danced

☞ To form the past tense of one-syllable verbs that end with a vowel and a consonant, double the final consonant. Then add *ed*.

hum–hummed　　　　　　stop–stopped

☞ To form the past tense of verbs that end with a consonant and *y*, change the *y* to *i* and add *ed*.

try–tried　　　　　　hurry–hurried

✏ **Practice**

Finish each sentence. Use the past-tense form of the verb in ( ).

**1.** In the parade, the drummers _____. (drum)

**2.** The people _____ and _____. (listen, cheer)

**3.** The children _____ "Hooray!" (cry)

**4.** The clowns _____ by. (hurry)

**5.** People on the floats _____. (wave)

**6.** The sirens of the fire engines _____. (wail)

**7.** Everyone _____ the parade. (watch)

**8.** After the horses _____ by, the parade _____. (trot, end)

Name _____ Date _____

## Verbs Working Together

☞ A **linking verb** connects the subject with the other words in the predicate. It tells what the subject *is* or *was*.

The people <u>were</u> hungry during the famine.

☞ The verb *be* is most often used as a linking verb. Some forms of *be* are *am, is, are, was,* and *were.*

Drought and famine <u>are</u> hard on everyone.

☞ Sometimes the verb is made up of two or more words. The **main verb** tells about the action.

☞ A **helping verb** helps the main verb express an action or make a statement.

Soon, the clouds <u>will release</u> the rain.

The words below are often used as helping verbs.

| am | is | are | was | were |
|------|------|------|------|------|
| have | has | had | will | |

✏ **Practice**

Read each sentence and find the verb in each. Underline each *linking verb* once. Underline each *main verb with a helping verb* twice.

1. Very few people were in the prairie.

2. The crops were dying.

3. The people had given all their energy to growing their crops.

4. They were hoping for rain.

5. No rain had fallen for weeks.

6. When they awoke, the rain was soaking the ground.

Name _____ Date _____

☞ **Irregular verbs** are verbs that do not add *ed* to show past tense.

Many farmers <u>grow</u> crops in the Central Plains.

They <u>grew</u> corn and wheat last year.

☞ Some irregular verbs show past time by using a different form of the main verb with *have, has,* or *had.*

People <u>write</u> about America.

They <u>have written</u> many stories.

| Verb | Present | Past | Verb with Have, Has, or Had |
|------|---------|------|------------------------------|
| begin | begin(s) | began | begun |
| come | come(s) | came | come |
| give | give(s) | gave | given |
| go | go(es) | went | gone |
| ring | ring(s) | rang | rung |
| run | run(s) | ran | run |
| sing | sing(s) | sang | sung |
| write | write(s) | wrote | written |
| find | find(s) | found | found |
| make | make(s) | made | made |
| become | become(s) | became | become |
| tell | tell(s) | told | told |
| grow | grow(s) | grew | grown |
| build | build(s) | built | built |
| lead | lead(s) | led | led |

✎ **Practice**

Make each sentence show past time. Write the correct form of the verb in ( ).

1. The words "from sea to shining sea" have _____ from the song "America the Beautiful." (come)

2. People _____ to settle in the United States centuries ago. (begin)

3. They _____ the words "Let freedom ring" in a song called "America." (sing)

**Go on to next page.**

Irregular Verbs
Unit One: Grammar
Language Arts 4, SV 3890-5

## Something Different, p. 2

✏ **Practice**

Make each sentence show past time. Write the correct form of the verb in ( ).

4. Some of the settlers had _____ farmers. (become)

5. Many years ago, pioneers _____ farms and ranches. (build)

6. The farms in the Central Plains have _____ the world a

   major supply of grain. (give)

7. Some other pioneers had _____ homes in

   the Appalachian Highlands. (make)

8. Miners _____ coal and petroleum there. (find)

9. Scouts had _____ pioneers across the dangerous

   Rocky Mountains. (lead)

10. They had _____ that this was the only way to reach the

    Pacific Coast. (find)

11. Many authors have _____ stories about pioneers crossing

    the Rocky Mountains. (write)

12. Last year, I _____ a trip across America. (take)

13. I _____ on the East Coast. (begin)

14. I started in New England and then _____ over the

    Appalachians. (go)

Name _____ Date _____

## Make It Interesting

☞ An **adjective** is a word that describes a noun.

   The <u>white</u> crane was <u>magnificent</u>.

☞ *A, an,* and *the* are special adjectives called **articles**. Use *a* before a singular noun or an adjective that begins with a consonant sound. Use *an* before a singular noun or an adjective that begins with a vowel sound.

   The bird became <u>a</u> girl.

   The maiden had <u>an</u> odd request.

### ✏ Practice

Complete these sentences with adjectives (adj.) and articles (art.). You may use the adjectives in the box.

| strong | poor | soft | injured |
|--------|------|------|---------|
| hurt   | kind | good | own     |

1. (Art.) _____ (adj.) _____ animal was caught in a trap.

2. Soon, (art.) _____ (adj.) _____ girl rescued the animal.

3. She took the (adj.) _____ animal to her (adj.) _____ house.

4. The girl put a bandage on (art.) _____ (adj.) _____ leg.

5. She gave the animal (art.) _____ (adj.) _____ bed in which

 to sleep.

6. Soon, the little animal was (adj.) _____ enough to take care

 of itself.

7. The animal and the girl remained (adj.) _____ friends.

**Adjectives**
**Unit One: Grammar**
Language Arts 4, SV 3890-5

Name _____  Date _____

## Compared to What?

☞ Adjectives can describe by comparing.

☞ One-syllable adjectives usually add *er* or *est* to make comparisons. Use *er* to compare two persons or things. Use *est* to compare more than two persons or things.

> Days on the farm seemed <u>duller</u> than days in the city.
> The first few days were the <u>slowest</u> of Thad's life.

☞ Adjectives of two or more syllables usually use *more* or *most* to make comparisons.

> The city was <u>more interesting</u> to Thad than the country.
> The farm was the <u>most boring</u> place in the world.

✏ **Practice**
Complete each sentence with the correct form of the adjective in ( ).

1. The horse was the _____ animal Jeannie had ever seen. (unusual)

2. She was _____ in the horse than in any other animal. (interested)

3. Before she saw the horse, the fair had seemed _____ than being at home. (dull)

4. Now it seemed like the _____ place in the world. (exciting)

5. The horse was the _____ one at the fair. (beautiful)

6. It was also the _____ horse there. (fast)

7. The horse was _____ than a gazelle. (graceful)

8. It was the _____ moment of Jeannie's life when she found she had won the horse. (thrilling)

Adjectives That Compare
Unit One: Grammar

Language Arts 4, SV 3890-5

Name _____ Date _____

## It's the Most!

☞ Add *er* or *est* to most adjectives to compare.
          old–older–oldest
          kind–kinder–kindest

☞ When an adjective ends with one vowel letter and one consonant letter, double the consonant letter before adding *er* or *est.*
          thin–thinner–thinnest

☞ When an adjective ends with *e,* drop the *e* before adding *er* or *est.*
          pale–paler–palest

☞ When an adjective ends with *y,* change the *y* to *i* before adding *er* or *est.*
          happy–happier–happiest

## ✐ Practice

Complete each sentence with the correct form of the adjective in ( ).

1. The first days on the farm were the _____ of the boy's life. (lonely)

2. He was _____ than usual until he read his sister's letter. (sad)

3. Then he wrote his sister an even _____ letter. (long)

4. The day the deer ran into the meadow, he

   felt _____ than ever. (lucky)

5. The deer was the _____ he had ever seen. (pretty)

6. Her steps were _____ than a cat's. (light)

7. The boy spent his _____ days waiting for the deer. (happy)

8. Seeing a deer was the _____ experience! (great)

**Adjectives That Compare**
**Unit One: Grammar**
Language Arts 4, SV 3890-5

Name _____ Date _____

## Describing Words

☞ An **adverb** is a word that tells more about a verb.

☞ Some adverbs tell *how* an action takes place. Most adverbs that tell *how* end in *ly*.
> The mice ran <u>quickly</u>.
> Their mother hid them <u>safely</u>.

☞ Some adverbs tell *when* an action takes place.
> The boys would be leaving <u>tomorrow</u>.
> <u>Then</u> they would travel by day.

☞ Some adverbs tell *where* an action takes place.
> They will stop <u>here</u> for the night.
> They will sleep <u>upstairs</u>.

✎ **Practice**

Complete the sentences with adverbs from the box that tell *how, when,* or *where.*

| | | | | |
|---|---|---|---|---|
| desperately | wearily | happily | loudly | proudly |
| busily | carefully | quietly | finally | here |

1. The girls were _____ cleaning the house.

2. They wanted _____ to surprise their mother.

3. They _____ cleaned every room.

4. The girls' mother walked _____ up the path.

5. Before she opened the door, the girls hid _____.

6. _____, she came into the house.

7. Their mother looked _____ at all the work they had done.

8. The girls _____ yelled, "Surprise! We are over _____!"

9. The girls smiled _____ when she thanked them.

**Adverbs**
**Unit One: Grammar**
Language Arts 4, SV 3890-5

Name _____ Date _____

## In Place of a Noun

☞ A **pronoun** is a word used in place of a noun or nouns.
> The traveler thought <u>he</u> should go to the city.

☞ A **subject pronoun** is a pronoun that is used as the subject of a sentence. The words *I, you, he she, it, we,* and *they* are subject pronouns.
> <u>She</u> shrugged and pointed.

☞ The pronouns *my, your, his, her, its, our,* and *their* are used in place of possessive nouns. They are called **possessive pronouns**.
> There is nothing exciting in <u>my</u> town.

☞ Some pronouns are formed by adding *self* and *selves. Myself, yourself, himself, herself,* and *itself* are singular pronouns. *Ourselves, yourselves,* and *themselves* are plural pronouns.
> The traveler walked off by <u>himself</u>.

✏ **Practice**

Use a pronoun in the second sentence to replace the underlined word or words in the first sentence.

1. <u>The farmer</u> planned a journey.

   _____ walked around his farm.

2. On his way he saw <u>a woman</u> washing clothes.

   _____ smiled at him and kept working.

3. <u>The farmer</u> heard of the city often.

   People told _____ that the city must be very exciting.

4. He saw <u>some women</u> on the hotel steps.

   _____ clothes were very stylish.

5. "I will be content on my farm now," said <u>the man</u>.

   "I will be happy to live on _____ little farm."

Name _____ Date _____

☞ The pronouns *me, you, him, her, it, us,* and *them* follow action verbs.

> Pa told <u>me</u> to bring a clock and a towel.
> I picked <u>him</u> for my very own.

✐ **Practice**

**A.** Pretend you are telling this story. Complete each sentence with a pronoun.

1. People had sent _____ lots of birthday cards.

2. I received _____ for my birthday.

3. "I will let _____ choose a puppy," said Pa to me.

4. When I saw the golden one, I wanted _____ so much!

5. "Take _____," smiled the owner.

6. Now the puppy follows _____ everywhere.

7. "Take good care of your pet," Pa said. "Most of all, give _____ lots of love and attention."

8. If you have a pet, be sure to love and protect _____.

**B.** Change the underlined word or words in each sentence to a pronoun. Write each pronoun on the line.

9. My puppy waits for <u>Pa and me</u> at the gate. _____

10. I throw <u>the puppy</u> a ball. _____

11. The puppy carries <u>the ball</u> in his mouth. _____

12. Everyone in my neighborhood knows <u>my puppy and me</u>. _____

Name _____ Date _____

## Pairing Up

 Some words are made by putting two smaller words together. The new word is a **compound word**. Compound words are usually written together as one word.

something        codfish        rattlesnake

### ✐ Practice

Write the paragraph on a separate piece of paper or the back of this sheet. Use the compound word from the box that matches each picture. Then circle the two words that form each compound.

| | | |
|---|---|---|
| Cornhusker | Yellowhammer | Sunflower |
| Sunshine | | Evergreen |

Almost every state has a nickname. This name is a symbol for the state. For

example, Alabama is known as the **1**  State. This nickname comes from

Alabama's state bird. Florida's nickname is the **2**  State. The states of

Kansas and Nebraska have interesting nicknames. Kansas is known as the

**3**  State. Nebraska's nickname is the **4**  State. If you like

bushes and trees, you might want to visit the **5** State of Washington.

**Compound Words**
**Unit One: Grammar**
Language Arts 4, SV 3890-5

Name _____ Date _____

☞ A **contraction** is a short way of writing two words together. Some of the letters are left out. An apostrophe (') takes their place.

it + is = it's          I + am = I'm
do + not = don't        is + not = isn't
you + will = you'll      let + us = let's
she + is = she's         where + is = where's

✏ **Practice**

Write contractions for the underlined words.

1. "<u>We are</u> going to play a practical joke at our Halloween party," I said. _____

2. "<u>You are</u> going to tell everyone your head <u>is not</u> really a pumpkin?" my sister asked. _____  _____

3. "You think <u>that is</u> really funny, right?" I replied. _____

4. I continued, "<u>How is</u> this for an idea?" _____

5. "<u>We will</u> tell our guests <u>they are</u> eating worms!" _____ _____

6. "You <u>cannot</u> do that!" my sister said. _____

7. "Our friends <u>would not</u> stay! <u>You will</u> make people sick!" _____ _____

8. "<u>You have</u> no sense of humor!" I said. _____

9. Then I explained, "You <u>have not</u> caught on yet. We <u>are not</u> really going to serve worms!" _____ _____

10. My sister said, "You mean <u>they will</u> only think <u>they have</u> worms on their plates?" _____ _____

11. "Right," I answered. "All <u>it will</u> be is spaghetti!" _____

12. "When <u>we have</u> turned down the lights, <u>who is</u> going to notice?" my sister giggled. _____ _____

13. "<u>Let us</u> get started, then!" I said. _____

14. "We <u>do not</u> have much time before the guests arrive." _____

Name _____ Date _____

## Unit Two Assessment: Sentences

✎ Finish the sentences. Add a subject or a predicate of your own to make a complete sentence. Then circle the *simple predicate* and underline the *simple subject* in each sentence.

1. My entire family _____.

2. _____ loves to go to baseball games in the summer.

✎ Write whether each sentence is *declarative, interrogative, imperative,* or *exclamatory.*

3. What a huge animal! _____

4. Where did it come from? _____

5. It has been in the yard since this morning. _____

6. Keep your distance from it. _____

✎ Combine the sentences to make one sentence.

7. The prince lives in the palace. The king lives in the palace.

   _____

8. Cindi's doll has brown hair. Cindi's doll is wearing skates.

   _____

9. Raoul loved to draw. He made pictures of many animals.

   _____

10. He was feeling lonely. He was feeling sad. He was feeling tired.

   _____

✎ Add adjectives to make the sentences more interesting.

11. The _____ horse ran through the grass.

12. My house is the _____ one with the _____ gardens.

✎ Add detail words to make the sentences more effective.

13. The _____ owl often stands for knowledge.

14. The _____ boys _____ ate the plate of biscuits.

Name _____ Date _____

## What's in a Sentence?

☞ A **sentence** is a group of words that expresses a complete thought.
Arithmetic is the study of how numbers work.

☞ Every sentence has two parts. The **subject** is the part about which something is said. The **predicate** tells about the subject.

| Subject | Predicate |
|---|---|
| Multiplication tables | are learned by students. |

☞ The **complete subject** is all the words that make up the subject.
<u>My arithmetic homework</u> was not very easy.

☞ The **simple subject** is the key word or words in the complete subject.
The hardest <u>problems</u> had multiplication.

☞ The **complete predicate** is all the words that tell something about the complete subject.
In science class we <u>learned how clouds are formed</u>.

☞ The **simple predicate** is the key word or words in the predicate. The simple predicate is an action verb or linking verb together with any helping verbs.
This geography book <u>describes</u> lakes and rivers.

✎ **Practice**
Complete each sentence with a complete subject or a complete predicate.

1. A notebook _____.

2. _____ shows your teacher what you have learned.

3. _____ is the study of countries and people.

4. Language _____.

5. A sentence _____.

Name _____ Date _____

☞ A **declarative sentence** makes a statement. It ends with a period (**.**).

Sherlock Shoe is a detective.
This is not his real name.

☞ An **interrogative sentence** asks a question. It ends with a question mark (**?**).

Do you know what a detective does?
How does Sherlock solve cases?

☞ An **imperative sentence** gives a command or makes a request. It ends with a period (**.**).

Look for clues that will solve the mystery.
Help Sherlock discover the thief's identity.

☞ An **exclamatory sentence** shows strong feeling or surprise. It ends with an exclamation point (**!**).

What a good detective Sherlock is!
He is so clever!

✐ **Practice**

Read each sentence. Tell whether it is *declarative, interrogative, imperative,* or *exclamatory*. Then finish each sentence with the correct punctuation mark.

_____ **1.** How did Cindi's doll just disappear _____

_____ **2.** Sherlock was at the store _____

_____ **3.** Sherlock felt sure he could find the doll _____

_____ **4.** Be sure to think carefully _____

_____ **5.** Will he have to talk to everyone in the building _____

_____ **6.** A nurse gave Sherlock an important clue _____

_____ **7.** Cindi, watch out _____

_____ **8.** Do what you have to do, detectives _____

_____ **9.** Without knowing it, Tony admitted he was a thief _____

_____ **10.** Wow, that was smart thinking, Sherlock _____

Name _____ Date _____

## Putting Them Together

☞ A good writer may combine two sentences that have the same subject or predicate. The word *and* is often used to combine sentence parts.

☞ The subjects of two sentences may be combined.

> The prince lives in the palace.
> The king lives in the palace.
> The prince <u>and</u> the king live in the palace.

☞ The predicates of two sentences may be combined.

> The thick fog appeared.
> The thick fog covered the forest.
> The thick fog appeared <u>and</u> covered the forest.

---

### How to Combine Sentences with the Same Subject or Predicate

**1.** Use the word *and* between the subjects to combine sentences with the same predicate.

**2.** When you combine subjects, be sure you use the correct form of the verb.

**3.** Use the word *and* between the predicates to combine sentences with the same subject.

---

### ✐ Practice

On a separate piece of paper or the back of this one, rewrite this paragraph to make it more interesting to read. Combine some subjects and some predicates.

    The king wanted to find his son. The king offered a reward. Strong men searched for the prince. Wise men searched for the prince. One boy knew the secret places of the forest. This boy decided to look for the prince. He found the prince in a cave. He figured out how to free him. The prince ran all the way to the palace. The boy ran all the way to the palace.

Name _____ Date _____

## A Good Combination

☞ To avoid short, choppy sentences, a writer often combines adjectives that
describe the same subject.

Tucker was feeling lonely.
Tucker was feeling bored.
Tucker was feeling tired.
Tucker was feeling lonely, bored, <u>and</u> tired.

---

### How to Combine Sentences with Adjectives

**1.** Look for different adjectives that describe the same subject.
**2.** Use *and* to combine them.
**3.** Use commas to separate three or more adjectives in a row. This is called
  a **series**.

---

✏ **Practice**

Rewrite the body of this letter. Make it more interesting to read
by combining sentences.

June 28, 1999

Dear Jennifer,

  You'll never guess what happened today! My pig escaped from the barn. Have I
sent you his picture? He is only two months old. He is cute. He is pink. He is tiny.
Mr. Carter caught him. He gave him milk. The milk was sweet. The milk was warm.
My poor pig was so scared. He was tired. He was hungry. I'm so happy that he's safe.

                                        Love,
                                        Fiona

_____

_____

_____

_____

_____

_____

_____

## Smooth Writing

☞ A writer can join two choppy sentences with the word *and, but,* or *or*.

Raoul loved to draw.
He made pictures of many animals.
Raoul loved to draw, <u>and</u> he made pictures of many animals.

Raoul may draw a picture of an elephant.
He may draw a lion instead.
Raoul may draw a picture of an elephant, <u>or</u> he may draw a lion instead.

---

### How to Combine Sentences Using *and, but,* or *or*

1. Write the word *and, but,* or *or* between two sentences to combine them.
2. Be sure the connecting word makes the meaning of the combined sentences clear.
3. Use a comma before the word *and, but,* or *or* when two sentences are combined.

---

✏ **Practice**

Combine each pair of sentences. Use the word in parentheses ( ).

1. Do you like to draw? Do you like to paint? (or)

   _____

2. I can draw with crayons. I can draw with pencils. (or)

   _____

3. I'd like to paint now. I'll make a mess. (but)

   _____

4. I like old paintings. I like color photographs. (and)

   _____

5. I will take a drawing class. I might take a painting class. (or)

   _____

6. Right now I'm drawing. I'd rather paint. (but)

   _____

Name _____  Date _____

## Be Exact

☞ A good writer uses **exact verbs**. Exact verbs clearly describe actions. They make sentences more interesting to read, and they help the audience to better understand the writer's meaning.

The children <u>walked</u> to the hayloft.
The children <u>marched</u> to the hayloft.

Ryan <u>lifted</u> himself into the loft.
Ryan <u>hoisted</u> himself into the loft.

---

**How to Write Sentences with Exact Verbs**
1. Think about the idea or action that you want your audience to understand.
2. Select several words that describe the action precisely.
3. Choose the clearest word to describe each action.

---

✎ **Practice**

Think of an exact verb to replace each underlined verb. Write your new verb on the line.

1. The children <u>made</u> _____ a pumpkin head.

2. Then they <u>looked</u> _____ for some old clothes.

3. They all <u>went</u> _____ up into the hayloft.

4. An owl <u>looked</u> _____ at the children from the corner of the loft.

5. Father <u>ran</u> _____ toward the barn frantically.

6. Father <u>spoke</u> _____ with fright.

7. The man <u>went</u> _____ out of the loft onto the ground.

8. The children <u>spoke</u> _____ loudly.

Name _____ Date _____

**Say What You Mean**

☞ A writer can expand short sentences by adding exact details. The details should be colorful words that give the reader an exact picture of how something looks, sounds, or tastes. These details can also tell more about how something moves or feels.

Americans chose the eagle as their symbol.
Americans <u>proudly</u> chose the <u>bald</u> eagle as their <u>national</u> symbol.

---
**How to Expand Sentences**
1. Look for sentences that do not give a clear picture of your idea.
2. Think of describing words that give a more exact picture.
3. Add these words to your sentences.
---

✏ **Practice**
Add detail words to these sentences to make them more interesting to read.

1. The _____ owl has often stood for knowledge.

2. People have thought that the bird's _____ eyes showed wisdom.

3. The _____ bear was a symbol for many warriors.

4. These warriors _____ carried their symbol into battle.

5. The _____ Chinese dragon is another symbol.

6. People often think of the _____ koala bear as the symbol

for Australia.

7. This _____ animal is not on Australia's coat of arms.

8. Peace is often symbolized by a _____ dove.

Name _____ Date _____

## Unit Three Assessment: Vocabulary and Usage

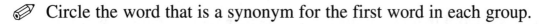 Circle the word that is a synonym for the first word in each group.

1. mad          terrible      angry       frightened
2. sprouted     grew          reached     followed
3. gorgeous     beautiful     amazing     pleasant

Circle the word that is an antonym for the first word in each group.

4. serious      likeable      silly       intelligent
5. start        finish        break       old
6. seldom       hardly        usually     never

Circle the prefix or suffix in each word.

7. artist

8. unlucky

9. tasteless

10. impossible

11. flexible

12. patiently

13. redo

14. inactive

15. hopeful

Circle the correct word or words to complete each sentence.

16. There are (two, too) many people in the boat.

17. He had sand in his (I, eye).

18. There are (ate, eight) of us for dinner.

19. When (I, me) grow up, I want to be an architect.

20. Will you show (I, me) how to knit?

21. We (enjoy, enjoys) being together.

22. She (look, looks) a little worried.

23. That is not (you're, your) wallet.

24. (Their, There) are so many places to visit (hear, here).

25. (I, Me) am so excited to be here!

Name _____ Date _____

## Similar Meanings

☞ A **synonym** is a word that has almost the same meaning as another word. Here are some synonyms for the word *brave*.

**brave**   adventurous, bold, courageous, daring, fearless

✐ **Practice**
Read each sentence. Replace each underlined word with a synonym. You can use a thesaurus to find synonyms.

1. Life in the village was <u>terrible</u>. _____

2. The bravest warriors could not fight off their <u>strong</u> enemy. _____

3. The <u>leader</u> of the village gave them advice. _____

4. He said, "You must <u>find</u> a way other than fighting." _____

5. One <u>courageous</u> girl knew what to do. _____

6. She <u>asked</u> her father to make the other warriors sit and talk with the enemy.

   _____

7. He agreed to try and <u>told</u> his plan to the other warriors. _____

8. Then something <u>amazing</u> happened. _____

9. The two enemies agreed to stop <u>arguing</u>. _____

10. The land was <u>quiet</u> again. _____

11. Once more, the people led <u>contented</u> lives. _____

12. They had found a way to avoid <u>trouble</u>. _____

Name _____ Date _____

## Opposite Meanings

☞ An **antonym** is a word that means the opposite of another word. Here are some antonyms for the word *lazy*.

      **lazy**   lively, active, busy, energetic, exciting, spirited

✎ **Practice**

Read each sentence. Write an antonym for the underlined word or words in each sentence. You can use a thesaurus to find antonyms.

1. On a <u>cold</u> _____ day, a <u>large</u> _____ bird

   landed on a hippo's back.

2. The hippo became very <u>calm</u> _____ .

3. He wanted to <u>pull</u> _____ the bird off.

4. The bird <u>laughed</u> _____ and begged the hippo to save him.

5. The bird said, "If you do, I will eat the <u>few</u> _____ bugs on

   your body that are always making you itch."

6. The <u>tiny</u> _____ hippo thought this was very <u>serious</u>

   _____ , and he agreed to leave the bird alone.

7. <u>Slowly</u> _____ the bird gobbled up the bugs.

8. Finally the bird <u>started</u> _____ .

9. The hippo had <u>always</u> _____ felt so comfortable.

10. He realized it was <u>false</u> _____ that a little animal could

    help a big one.

**Antonyms**
**Unit Three: Vocabulary and Usage**
Language Arts 4, SV 3890-5

Name _____ Date _____

## Change the Meaning

☞ A **prefix** is a letter or group of letters added to the beginning of a base word. Adding a prefix to a word changes the word's meaning.

> The prince said he <u>liked</u> being in the cave.
> He <u>disliked</u> the way the kingdom was run.

☞ A **base word** is a word to which other word parts may be added.

| Prefix | Meaning | Example |
|--------|-----------|-----------|
| dis | not | <u>dis</u>like |
| im | not | <u>im</u>possible |
| in | not | <u>in</u>active |
| mis | incorrectly | <u>mis</u>label |
| non | not | <u>non</u>stop |
| pre | before | <u>pre</u>pay |
| re | again | <u>re</u>read |
| re | back | <u>re</u>pay |
| un | not | <u>un</u>kind |
| un | opposite of | <u>un</u>button |

 **Practice**

Read each sentence. Add a prefix with the meaning in ( ) to each underlined word. Use the list above to help you.

1. Tony was <u>fair</u> to keep the doll. (not) _____

2. He waited <u>patiently</u> for Cindi's reaction. (not) _____

3. Sherlock <u>planned</u> how he would look for the doll. (before) _____

4. Tony <u>understood</u> Sherlock's interest in the doll. (incorrectly) _____

5. Tony <u>covered</u> the doll's hiding place. (opposite of) _____

6. Sherlock <u>traced</u> Tony's path. (again) _____

7. At first, Cindi <u>trusted</u> Sherlock. (not) _____

8. She thought he was <u>capable</u> of finding the doll. (not) _____

Name _____ Date _____

## After Word

☞ A **suffix** is a letter or group of letters added to the end of a base word. Adding a suffix to a word changes the word's meaning.

The tired <u>hiker</u> rested <u>quietly</u>.

☞ A **base word** is a word to which other word parts may be added.

| Suffix | Meaning | Example |
|--------|---------|---------|
| al | like, referring to | coast<u>al</u> |
| able, ible | able to be | break<u>able</u>, flex<u>ible</u> |
| er, or | one who | sing<u>er</u>, sail<u>or</u> |
| ful | full of | help<u>ful</u> |
| less | without | home<u>less</u> |
| y | what kind | snow<u>y</u> |
| ly | how | quick<u>ly</u> |
| ist | one who does | art<u>ist</u> |

✎ **Practice**

Choose a suffix from the list above. Add it to the word in ( ). Then write the word in the blank.

1. It was a dark, (storm) night. _____

2. A (visit) scratched at my door. _____

3. I opened the door and saw a white bear that must have been (home).

   _____

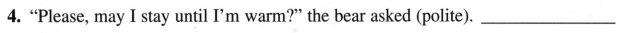

4. "Please, may I stay until I'm warm?" the bear asked (polite). _____

5. The bear's (music) voice relaxed me. _____

6. He told me (wonder) stories by the fire. _____

7. They were (magic) stories, full of interesting characters. _____

8. One was about some (remark) creatures that could change from bears to

   people. _____

9. Next morning this (friend) bear was gone. _____

10. In its place was a (delight) man with long white hair. _____

Name _____ Date _____

## Some Little Riddles

☞ **Homographs** are words that have the same spelling but different meanings. Sometimes homographs have different pronunciations.

> We saw a <u>seal</u> at the zoo.
> Be sure you <u>seal</u> the envelope before you mail it.
>
> Some animals <u>live</u> on land and water.
> <u>Live</u> plants are not allowed in this building.

✏ **Practice**

Read each riddle. Tell what the underlined word means in each riddle. Then write a sentence to show a different meaning for each underlined word.

**1.** Question: What never comes up when you are <u>down</u>?

   Answer: your smile

   Meaning: _____

   Your Sentence: _____

**2.** Question: Why did the boy throw the clock out the window?

   Answer: to see how time <u>flies</u>

   Meaning: _____

   Your Sentence: _____

**3.** Question: What piece of furniture do you carry in your head?

   Answer: the multiplication <u>table</u>

   Meaning: _____

   Your Sentence: _____

**4.** Question: How did the giant show that he enjoyed the concert?

   Answer: by giving the musicians a big <u>hand</u>

   Meaning:_____

   Your Sentence: _____

Name _____ Date _____

☞ **Homophones** are words that sound alike. They are spelled differently and have different meanings.

> Beth did the <u>right</u> thing to help her allergy.
> Did she <u>write</u> a thank-you note to the doctor?

> "Please <u>be</u> my friend!" Beth begged.
> Beth was not allergic to <u>bee</u> stings.

✏ **Practice**

Complete each sentence correctly. Choose the correct homophone in ( ) and write it in the blank.

1. The dirt road leading to the farm _____ the highway. (meats, meets)

2. The girl _____ the sign that told her about the puppies. (red, read)

3. _____ the man sell her a puppy? (Would, Wood)

4. The girl thought it would be hard to _____ a puppy. (choose, chews)

5. The girl thought she could _____ her mother. (hear, here)

6. When she reached the turn, she saw her _____ yellow house.

   (pail, pale)

7. Her mother said she _____ nothing about any puppies. (new, knew)

8. The puppy wagged his _____. (tail, tale)

9. He would _____ for the girl to come home from school.

   (wait, weight)

10. The puppy jumped on her when he _____ his name. (herd, heard)

Name _____ Date _____

## In Brief

☞ An **abbreviation** is a short way of writing a word or words.

☞ Here are abbreviations for titles of people.

    Mr.            Ms.            Mrs.            Dr.

☞ Here are some common street abbreviations.

| | | |
|---|---|---|
| Street–St. | Avenue–Ave. | Highway–Hwy. |
| Road–Rd. | Drive–Dr. | Place–Pl. |

☞ Here are the abbreviations for the days of the week and the months of the year.

| | | |
|---|---|---|
| Sunday–Sun. | Monday–Mon. | |
| Tuesday–Tues. | Wednesday–Wed. | |
| Thursday–Thurs. | Friday–Fri. | Saturday–Sat. |

| | | |
|---|---|---|
| January–Jan. | February–Feb. | March–Mar. |
| April–Apr. | August–Aug. | September–Sept. |
| October–Oct. | November–Nov. | December–Dec. |

## ✐ Practice

Write the correct abbreviation for the underlined word or words.

1. Susan came from Harbor <u>Drive</u>. _____

2. She said, "I couldn't stay away, <u>Doctor</u> Crane." _____

3. "My toe has been hurting since <u>Saturday</u>." _____

4. Then <u>Mister</u> Brown came into my office on Andy <u>Avenue</u>. _____

5. "There has been a crime on Raburn <u>Street</u>!" _____

6. "The cow that I bought last <u>January</u> is gone!" _____

Name _____ Date _____

## Do You Two Want to Go, Too?

☞ Use *to* when you mean "in the direction of." Use *too* when you mean "also" or "more than enough." Use *two* when you mean "one more than one."

> We went <u>to</u> the stand and bought <u>two</u> lemonades.
> Stewart bought a cup, <u>too</u>.

☞ Use *your* when you mean "belonging to you." Use *you're* when you mean "you are." *You're* is a contraction for *you are*.

> <u>You're</u> earning money.
> You will get <u>your</u> mitt soon.

## ✏ Practice

**A.** Complete each sentence correctly. Choose and circle the correct word in ( ).

1. (Your, You're) going to love these new running shoes.

2. No sneakers ever felt so good on (your, you're) feet.

3. (You're, Your) feet will feel great.

4. They will be so happy, (to, two, too).

5. Get (two, too, to) the store and buy a pair.

6. In fact, why don't you buy (two, to, too) pairs?

7. Buy a pair for your mother, (to, two, too).

8. We promise that (you're, your) not going to be sorry.

9. (Your, You're) feet will thank you.

10. (Your, You're) wallet will, (to, too, two).

**B.** The underlined word in each sentence is spelled incorrectly. Write the correct word.

11. Do you feel <u>to</u> tired every morning?_____

12. Does <u>you're</u> life need more pep and zip? _____

13. If <u>your</u> going to say "yes," try new Full o' Fun cereal. _____

14. It has all the good things <u>you're</u> body needs. _____

15. It has plenty of fiber, <u>two</u>. _____

**Troublesome Words**
**Unit Three: Vocabulary and Usage**
Language Arts 4, SV 3890-5

## They're There, Now!

☞ Use *their* when you mean "belonging to them."

Their trick is very clever.

☞ Use *there* when you mean "in that place."

The scooter is over there.

☞ Use *they're* when you mean "they are." *They're* is a contraction for *they are.*

They're going to fool their father.

✎ **Practice**

**A.** Read each sentence. Choose and circle the correct word in ( ).

1. The Browns are fed up with (there, their) neighbor.

2. (They're, Their) going to play the greatest practical joke ever.

3. (Their, There) are all the things they need.

4. (They're, Their) going to use the wagon.

5. This time (they're, there) going to have the last laugh.

6. Even (their, there) pets will get into the act.

7. The neighbor will never want to go (their, there) again!

8. The Browns will laugh at (their, there) successful joke.

**B.** Complete each sentence correctly. Write *their, there,* or *they're* in the blank.

9. _____ on the hill is a house.

10. Do people who lived _____ long ago still walk the halls at night?

11. They think it's still _____ house.

12. _____ not going to let anyone else live _____ peacefully!

Name _____ Date _____

## Are You Well? That's Good!

☞ The word *good* is an adjective. It describes a noun.
  The pig had a <u>good</u> life on the farm.

☞ The word *well* is an adverb. It tells more about a verb.
  The pig was treated <u>well</u> there.

✏ **Practice**

A. Complete each sentence with the correct word. Circle your choice.

1. Tom had a (well, good) home, but he was bored.

2. He searched for some (good, well) food to eat.

3. He went hunting and found something (good, well).

4. The goose gave Tom a (well, good) idea.

5. All the animals heard the (good, well) news.

6. Tom thought it would be a (good, well) feeling to be free.

7. Tom thought he did (good, well) to return to his pen.

B. Complete each sentence correctly. Add *good* or *well*. Then circle the word in each sentence that *good* or *well* tells more about.

8. Tom was a _____ pig.

9. But sometimes things did not go _____ for him.

10. Some days he didn't have _____ thoughts about his life.

11. He discovered that the outside world was a _____ place.

12. _____ things don't always last, though.

13. Events do not always turn out _____.

14. Tom's _____ time was soon over.

© Steck-Vaughn Company

**Troublesome Words**
**Unit Three: Vocabulary and Usage**
Language Arts 4, SV 3890-5

Name _____ Date _____

## I and Me

☞ The word *I* is always used in the subject part of the sentence.
> I wanted a puppy. Dad and I drove to the country.

☞ The word *me* follows an action verb.
> Dad took me to the barn. The man gave me a puppy.

✎ **Practice**

**A.** Choose and circle the word in ( ) that correctly completes each sentence.

1. (Me, I) was celebrating my seventh birthday.

2. My father and (I, me) rode in the car.

3. People had sent (I, me) many birthday cards.

4. (I, Me) brought them along on the trip.

5. Soon Dad and (me, I) arrived at a house in the country.

6. A lady there showed (I, me) her dog.

7. (I, Me) was so excited!

8. Oh, how (me, I) wanted a puppy for my very own!

9. One of the puppies wanted (me, I), too.

10. The smallest one kept (me, I) company all the way home.

**B.** Complete each sentence correctly. Use *I* or *me*.

11. A friend brought _____ a special birthday gift.

12. _____ had always wanted a pet parakeet.

13. At first _____ left him alone so he could get used to his new cage.

14. Before too long, my parakeet trusted _____.

15. My little bird loved _____.

16. He greeted _____ with cheerful chirping.

17. He allowed _____ to train him to do all kinds of tricks.

18. My bird and _____ put on shows for my friends.

Name _____ Date _____

## Its or It's

☞ Use *its* when you mean "belonging to it."

An armadillo uses <u>its</u> armor for protection.

☞ Use *it's* when you mean "it is." *It's* is a contraction for *it is.*

<u>It's</u> necessary for animals to defend themselves.

✏ **Practice**

**A.** Complete each sentence correctly. Use *its* or *it's.*

1. A turtle can pull _____ head, tail, and legs into a shell.

2. _____ a good thing the turtle can do this.

3. Otherwise, _____ enemies might destroy it.

4. Many animals have learned that _____ unwise to try to attack a porcupine.

5. An animal called an ermine protects _____ life by changing to a white color in winter.

6. Because of this, _____ hard for the ermine's enemies to see it against a snowy background.

7. The chameleon can change color to match _____ background.

8. _____ amazing to watch this animal turn green.

9. I think _____ interesting to study animals.

10. Each kind of animal has _____ own enemies.

**B.** Find and circle the incorrect spellings of *its* and *it's* in the paragraph.

Its a fact that animals do not kill each other for fun. For example, one animal might attack another in order to feed it's family. Because every animal has it's enemies, each one has it's own way to defend it's life, it's home, and it's young.

**Troublesome Words**
**Unit Three: Vocabulary and Usage**
Language Arts 4, SV 3890-5

Name _____ Date _____

☞ A verb must agree with its subject in number. Use a singular verb when the subject of the sentence is singular. Use a plural verb when the subject of the sentence is plural.

The <u>boy</u> <u>searches</u> near and far.
The wisest <u>men</u> <u>search</u> far and wide.

✎ **Practice**

**A.** Complete each sentence correctly. Choose and circle the correct form of the verb in ( ).

1. Thick, cold fog (blow, blows) in from nowhere.

2. The cave (are, is) completely covered.

3. The king (promise, promises) half his kingdom as a reward.

4. Practically everyone in the kingdom (look, looks) for the prince.

5. A boy (discover, discovers) the prince in a cave.

6. Two witches (put, puts) a spell on him.

7. They (say, says) a secret rhyme.

8. The prince (refuse, refuses) to fall under their spell.

9. The boy and the prince (escape, escapes) safely.

**B.** Complete each sentence with the correct form of the verb in ( ).

10. The boy _____ half the kingdom. (earn)

11. He _____ he is a wise ruler. (prove)

12. The boy and the prince _____ many adventures together. (enjoy)

Name _____ Date _____

## Unit Four Assessment: Capitalization and Punctuation

✏ Add the correct punctuation to each sentence. Use *periods, question marks, exclamation points, commas, colons, apostrophes, underlines,* and *quotation marks.*

1. That was a great play, said Susan

2. Mrs Beasley is the only person who didnt come

3. Larry likes the way his car looks now

4. Does class begin at 300 P M or 230 P M

5. What a horrible ending

6. Have you read the book the long trail home?

7. I wrote a poem called Frost on the Windows.

8. School has been fun this year

9. We went on a field trip to Boston Massachusetts

10. We went on May 4 1999.

✏ Write the sentences again using capital letters where they are needed.

11. susan says that the best holiday is thanksgiving day.

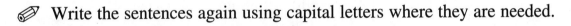
_____

_____

12. that is the last time I will give joe carmel a ride in my car!

_____

13. dr. jones was the last one here, and he left at 3:15 a.m.

_____

14. tell me if you like the book gone with the wind.

_____

Name _____ Date _____

## Good Beginnings

☞ Use a capital letter to begin the first word of a sentence.
   Today we solved some arithmetic problems.

☞ Use a capital letter to begin the first word, the last word, and all other important words in the title of a book, a story, a magazine article, a poem, a song, or a television show.

   Millions of Cats (book)
   "Numbers and You" (story)

### ✎ Practice
Read each sentence. Circle the letters that should be capital letters.

1. school started last week.

2. this year I have a new teacher.

3. her name is Ms. Aarvig.

4. she has given us some interesting arithmetic problems.

5. some of the problems were even funny.

6. we had to figure out some strange things.

7. the problems took a long time to solve.

8. our group was the first one finished.

9. the answers we got were really amazing.

10. One of my favorite books is the amazing number machine.

11. My brother is reading the story "the math magician."

12. My teacher read aloud the article "it all adds up."

13. Have you ever read the poem "crazy eights"?

Name _____  Date _____

## Names and I

☞ Begin each part of the name of a person with a capital letter.

        Tony Treworgy           Sherlock S. Shoe

☞ Begin a title of a person, such as *Ms., Mrs., Mr.,* or *Dr.,* with a capital letter.

        Ms. Cindi Sample        Dr. Vera Wesley

☞ Always capitalize the word *I*.

        I know I have a dentist appointment today.

✏ **Practice**

Read each sentence. Circle the letters that should be capital letters.

1. sherman smith has an unusual nickname.

2. His nickname is sherlock shoe.

3. Someone took cindi's doll.

4. the only suspect is tony treworgy.

5. dr. Wesley does not have the doll.

6. dr. Carter treated a boy the same morning.

7. mrs. Smith told Sherlock to ask capt. Kent for help.

8. Did you see where i left my doll?

9. i cannot believe that i lost it.

10. i am going to tony treworgy's house.

11. i know i left my doll in the waiting room.

12. How will i solve this mystery?

Name _____ Date _____

## Names of Places

☞ Begin each important word in the names of towns, cities, states, and countries and their abbreviations with a capital letter.

Anchorage, Alaska–AK          United States–U.S.

☞ Begin the names of streets and their abbreviations with a capital letter.

Fox Avenue–Ave.          Mukluk Boulevard–Blvd.
Glacier Street–St.          Caribou Drive–Dr.

✎ **Practice**

Read each sentence. Circle the letters that should be capital letters.

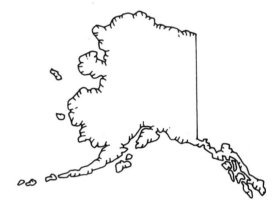

1. I am proud that alaska is the largest state.

2. alaska's eastern neighbor is canada.

3. The state capital of alaska is juneau.

4. I have visited mt. mcKinley with my father.

5. I would like to visit the aleutian islands.

6. My father tells stories about the copper mines at kennicott.

7. He once mined gold along the stikine river.

8. My father fishes along the yukon river.

9. He also likes to visit anchorage.

10. I live on nyac street.

11. The grocery store is at the corner of blizzard avenue.

12. The dogsled flies along husky boulevard.

13. My grandmother lives on harpoon lane.

14. elk circle is the location of my new school.

Name _____ Date _____

## Days, Months, and Holidays

☞ Begin the name of a day of the week or its abbreviation with a capital letter.

        Sunday–Sun.       Thursday–Thurs.

☞ Begin the name of a month or its abbreviation with a capital letter.

        August–Aug.       September–Sept.

☞ Begin each important word in the name of a holiday or special day with a capital letter.

        Thanksgiving       Fourth of July

✏ **Practice**

Read each sentence. Circle the letters that should be capital letters.

1. The boys arrived in Philadelphia on thursday.

2. friday morning they found their father.

3. All day saturday they slept.

4. They celebrated John's birthday on sunday.

5. Their journey started in july.

6. It was during august when they reached Philadelphia.

7. In september the boys started school.

8. They received a message from their mother october 2.

9. She would join them on halloween.

10. The entire family would be together on thanksgiving.

11. They would celebrate christmas together.

12. The boys planned to show their mother on new year's day that they could read.

Name _____ Date _____

## Periods in Place

☞ Use a **period** (.) at the end of a declarative or imperative sentence.
        Arithmetic adds up to answers.

☞ Use a period after an abbreviation.
        P.S.      U.S.      Tues.      Oct.
        Dr.       A.M.      Mr.      Mrs.

☞ Use a period after an initial.
        Jason M. Dawson

☞ Use a period after the numeral in a main topic and after the capital letter in a subtopic of an outline.

        I.  How to Master Multiplication
           A.  Learn multiplication tables
           B.  Practice doing multiplication problems

✏ **Practice**

Correct each item. Add periods where they are needed.

1. The new arithmetic books are red and yellow

2. Arithmetic is my first class every morning

3. Pages full of arithmetic problems are a challenge

4. Mr Washington is my arithmetic teacher this year

5. Class starts every day at 8:15 A M

6. Sometimes Dr Pritchett attends our class

7. Sally N Right is the smartest girl in my arithmetic class

8. T C Russell won an award at the arithmetic fair

9. I shared my book today with J D Kline

10.          I  Arithmetic Every Day
           A  In the classroom
           B  At home
           C  At the store

Name _____  Date _____

## Questions and Exclamations

☞ Use a **question mark (?)** at the end of an interrogative sentence.

Who stole the roller skates?

☞ Use an **exclamation point (!)** at the end of an exclamatory sentence.

I cannot imagine stealing from a detective!

✐ **Practice**

Finish each sentence with the correct end punctuation mark.

1. Do you enjoy reading mysteries

2. They are also exciting to read

3. Which mystery writers are your favorites

4. Donald Sobol writes terrific mysteries

5. He really keeps you guessing

6. Have you ever read the mystery series about Amy Adams and Hawkeye Collins

7. What wonderful stories they are

8. Nancy Drew mysteries are the greatest

9. How does Nancy solve her mysteries so quickly

10. She is a natural sleuth

11. Would you like to be a detective

12. That is a great idea

13. What case would you like to solve first

14. How about a tough one

15. What a great way to start

16. What is the case

17. How about helping me find my keys

18. What a funny detective you are

## The Comma

☞ Use a **comma** (,) in an address to separate the city and state or the city and country.

Anchorage, Alaska        Toronto, Canada

☞ Use a comma between the day and the year.

January 19, 1999        August 7, 1999

☞ Use a comma after the greeting of a friendly letter and after the closing of any letter.

Dear Gramma,        Your granddaughter,

### ✎ Practice

Write each item correctly. Add commas where they are needed.

1. 45 Harper Road
   Icetown Alaska 99682
   November 15 1999

2. 8260 Polar Lane
   Winter Park Florida 32792
   August 2 1999

3. 94 Klondike Circle
   Juneau Alaska 99673
   December 23 1999

4. 69 Tundra Avenue
   Yonkers New York 10710
   June 27 1999

5. Dear Aunt Rita

6. Sincerely yours

7. Dear Mother

8. Your friend

9. Dear Apah

10. Your sister

11. Dear Mika

12. Love

## Yes, You Do Need a Comma!

☞ Use a **comma** (,) after the words *yes* and *no* when they begin a statement.
    Yes, the boys should join their father.

☞ Use a comma after time-order words such as *first, next, then,* and *last.*
    First, the boys must have a plan.

☞ Use commas to separate three or more words in a series.
    The boys ran quickly, silently, and anxiously.

☞ Use a comma before the word *and, but,* or *or* when two sentences are combined.
    Josh felt tired, but he continued to run.

☞ Use a comma to separate a word used in direct address from a sentence.
    Andy, I need to rest for a minute.

☞ Use a comma between a quotation and the rest of the sentence.
    "We are almost there," said Andy.

### ✎ Practice

Read each sentence. Add commas where they are needed.

1. Yes Mr. and Mrs. Saxby helped the boys.

2. First he told them about the plan.

3. The boys studied letters words and maps.

4. Mr. Saxby talked about Searsville Richmond Washington and Philadelphia.

5. Mr. Saxby had a map but the boys lost the map.

6. Mrs. Saxby pasted a label on a jar and she put jelly in it.

7. Andy you must pretend that this is not yours.

8. "Travel by day" said Mr. Saxby.

Name _____ Date _____

## Using Apostrophes and Colons

☞ Add an **apostrophe** (') and *s* to singular nouns to show possession.

Erika's parka          Father's tools

☞ Add an apostrophe to a plural noun that ends in *s* to show possession.

seals' oil          guests' laughter

☞ Add an apostrophe and *s* to plural nouns that do not end in *s* to show possession.

women's advice          children's schoolwork

☞ Use an apostrophe to show that one or more letters have been left out of a contraction.

I will–I'll          do not–don't

☞ Use a **colon** (:) between the hour and minute in the time of day.

10:30 A.M.          8:15 P.M.

✏ **Practice**

Correct each sentence. Add apostrophes and colons where they are needed.

**1.** Erikas birthday was on a cold winter day.

**2.** The childrens faces lit up when they saw the snow.

**3.** The two girls walk home was difficult.

**4.** Her mothers voice greeted Erika.

**5.** "We dont have everything for your party."

**6.** "I ll go with you to the store," Erika replied.

**7.** "Wheres Father?" Erika asked.

**8.** "Well look for your father on the way to the store."

**9.** She added, "Father left at 6 30 this morning."

**10.** "I left school at 1 15 this afternoon," said Erika.

Name _____ Date _____

## Quotation Marks and Underlines

☞ Use **quotation marks** (" ") before and after a direct quotation.

Trudi moaned, "I'll never have a dog!"

"You're allergic to them," said Dr. Baxter.

☞ Use quotation marks before and after the title of a story or poem.

"An Allergy Is a Bothersome Thing" (story)

"Noses" (poem)

☞ Underline the title of a book or a television show.

<u>All About Allergies</u> (book)

<u>It's a Dog's Life</u> (television show)

✏ **Practice**

A. Complete the sentences correctly. Add quotation marks where they are needed.

1. Dad is bringing home a puppy today, Trudi said.

2. What kind of puppy will he choose? asked Donald.

3. Trudi said, I asked for a pug.

4. Where is my puppy? Trudi asked.

5. Go into the yard, Trudi, her mother replied.

6. Is it in the yard? Trudi asked eagerly.

7. Trudi wrote a poem called My Puppy.

8. She read a story called Our Dog Dan.

B. Read the sentences. Add underlines where they are needed.

9. Trudi read the book How to Be a Good Master.

10. Then, she watched the television show Lassie.

11. She read The Alphabet Book to her baby brother.

12. Next, she will read A Trip to the Zoo to him.

Name _____ Date _____

## Unit Five Assessment: Kinds of Writing

✏ Look at the picture. Choose one of the kinds of writing in the box. Circle your choice. Write about the picture using the kind of writing you chose. Use the back of this paper or another piece of paper for your writing.

Note: Be sure to follow the rules for good writing.
- If you are writing a story, write a beginning, a middle, and an ending.
- Give your main character a problem to solve.
- Write a conclusion; tell how your main character solved the problem.
- Write clear paragraphs with topic sentences and detail sentences.
- Give your writing a title.

---

**Kinds of Writing**

**story with dialogue** (beginning, middle, ending; solve a problem)
**poem** (paint a picture with words; use *rhyme* and *rhythm*)
**play** (give characters stage directions)
**news story** (tell about an event; tell *who, what, when, where, why*)
**magazine article** (nonfiction; give information about a topic)
**autobiography** (tell a story about your life)
**friendly letter** (use *heading, greeting, body, closing, signature*)
**invitation** (tell *who, what, when, where,* and *special information*)
**journal** (write date; list important events)

---

Name _____ Date _____

☞ A **story** tells about one main idea. Every story has an *introduction*, a *development*, and a *conclusion*.

## The Light of the Party

It was Halloween night, and Teresa was having a party. Suddenly there was a loud crack of thunder, and the room went black. The lights came on again but not in the living room. Then Teresa had an idea. She lit all the Halloween candles. Teresa's bright idea had saved the party.

---

**How to Write a Story**

**1.** Write an interesting introduction to present the main character and the setting.
**2.** Tell about a problem that the main character has to solve in the development. Tell about what happens in order.
**3.** Write a conclusion. Tell how the main character solves the problem or meets the challenge.
**4.** Write a title for your story.

---

✎ **Practice**
Finish this chart with information from the example story.

| Introduction | Development | Conclusion |
|---|---|---|
| Characters:<br><br><br>Setting: | Problem: | |

Name _____ Date _____

## What Did They Say?

☞ A writer uses **dialogue** to show how characters speak to one another.

"I can't think of a topic for my research report for Miss Shaw's class," Trudi moaned.

"Miss Shaw said we should write about something we already know a little about," reminded Carlos.

"Well, the thing I seem to know best these days is my allergy to dogs!" Trudi said, laughing.

---

**How to Write Story Dialogue**

1. Place quotation marks before and after a speaker's exact words.
2. Use a comma to separate a quotation from the rest of the sentence unless a question mark or exclamation point is needed.
3. Begin a new paragraph each time the speaker changes.
4. Be sure the conversation sounds like real people talking. Use words that tell exactly how the character speaks.

---

✐ **Practice**

Trudi goes to the library to research her report. Write a short conversation between Trudi and the librarian. Include words that tell how each person speaks.

_____

_____

_____

_____

_____

_____

_____

_____

_____

© Steck-Vaughn Company

**Story Dialogue**
**Unit Five: Kinds of Writing**
Language Arts 4, SV 3890-5

Name _____ Date _____

## Write a Poem

☞ In a **poem** a writer paints a picture or expresses a feeling with words. A writer often uses rhythm and rhyme in a poem. A writer may also use many words that begin with the same sound. Sometimes a writer compares two things using the word *like* or *as*.

### Halloween

Goblins, witches in the night,
Giving everyone a fright.
Creepy creaks on every stair,
Bats dark as night fly everywhere,
Look out—one is in your hair!
Hooray—it's Halloween!

---

### How to Write a Poem

**1.** Choose a topic for your poem.
**2.** Use colorful words to paint a picture for your audience.
**3.** Use rhyme and rhythm to help express feeling.
**4.** Use words that imitate sounds or words that begin with the same sound.
**5.** Make comparisons between two things that do not seem alike.
**6.** Give your poem a title.

---

✏ **Practice**

Finish this poem. Add colorful words that rhyme, compare, or add sound. Then give the poem a title.

_____

A jack-o-lantern's _____ smile

Glowed like a _____ in the _____ night,

Till an owl flew _____ with a _____ cry

And the _____ wind blew out the _____.

Name _____ Date _____

## Write a Play

☞ In a **play** a writer tells a story that is meant to be acted out. A play has characters, one or more settings, and a plot.

☞ The conversations between the characters in a play are called **dialogue**.

☞ A writer needs to include **stage directions** in a play. These are words that tell the characters how to move, act, and speak.

### The Missing Bus

Henry: (*Worried*) Where is that bus?
Dana: I don't know, but we're going to be late!
Peter: Maybe we should call home to tell them about the bus.
Dana: If we do that, they will know about our surprise!
Henry: (*Pointing down the street*) Look! Here comes the bus now.

---

### How to Write a Play

1. Use dialogue to tell the story. Let the characters' conversations explain the action.
2. Write clear stage directions that tell exactly how the characters act, move, and speak.
3. Be sure your play has an introduction, a development, and a conclusion.

---

✐ **Practice**

Pretend that the bus is so full that only one of the children can get on. Write dialogue for Dana, Peter, and Henry. Remember to include stage directions.

_____

_____

_____

_____

_____

_____

Name _____ Date _____

## In the News

☞ A **news story** gives information to the audience. It tells *who, what, when, where,* and sometimes *why* something happened.

☞ The **headline** is the title of a news story. A headline often contains a strong verb.

### Henry Hammers Home a Winner

Today in West Virginia John Henry proved he is the fastest and strongest steel driver in America. Mr. Henry raced against a steam drill and won. The race began at 11:30 A.M. In less than three hours, Mr. Henry had hammered by himself more dynamite holes into solid rock than the steam drill had drilled. Mr. Henry did so well that plans are being formed for him to race against an even more powerful machine.

---

### How to Write a News Story
1. Write a sentence that introduces the story.
2. Give details that tell *who, what, when, where,* and *why.*
3. Write a short, interesting headline. Use a strong verb to attract the audience. Begin each important word with a capital letter.

---

✐ **Practice**

Finish the chart with details from the example news story.

| Who? | What? | When? | Where? | Why? |
|------|-------|-------|--------|------|
|      |       |       |        |      |

Name _____  Date _____

☞ In a **magazine article** a writer gives information about a topic. A magazine article is **nonfiction**. This means that the information in the article is true.

### Soup's On!

Mamacita's Kitchen is an international restaurant with a special flavor. The owner, Maria Vasquez, provides a daily menu that features international soups. Today, tourists from around the world visit Mamacita's Kitchen. Many of them have even sent their favorite soup recipes to Ms. Vasquez. A diner might even find that his or her own recipe is on the menu that day. The four most popular soups are Mexicali, French Onion, Cuban Black Bean, and Italian Minestrone.

---

**How to Write a Magazine Article**
1. Write a sentence that introduces your subject.
2. Give facts about your subject in the detail sentences.
3. Write an interesting title for your magazine article.

---

✏ **Practice**

Pretend you are a reporter. Write three questions you would ask Ms. Vasquez about her restaurant.

Question 1: _____

_____

Question 2: _____

_____

Question 3: _____

_____

## All About You

☞ In an **autobiography** a writer tells about his or her life.

### My Story
by Cinderella

Once I lived with my stepmother and two stepsisters. They did not treat me well. I had to do all of the work. Then the prince had a ball. I did not have anything to wear, so I could not go. Then my fairy godmother appeared. She sent me to the prince's ball in a beautiful gown. At last, I was dancing with the prince!

> ### How to Write an Autobiography
> **1.** Use the pronouns *I, me,* and *my* to tell about yourself.
> **2.** Write about events in the order they happened.
> **3.** Use time-order words to help your audience follow the order of events.
> **4.** Write a title for your autobiography.

✏ **Practice**

Change the underlined words in the paragraph to continue the example autobiography. Write the new words in the blanks.

Cinderella _____ danced with the prince until midnight. She

_____ heard the clock chime and ran home. The prince looked for her

_____. He tried her _____ shoe on every girl in the

kingdom. Finally, the prince found Cinderella _____. They

_____ were married and lived happily ever after.

## To a Friend

☞ A **friendly letter** is a letter you write to someone you know. Every friendly letter has five parts.

**heading**
627 Swan Court
Raleigh, NC 27611
August 10, 1999

**greeting**
Dear Jason,

**body**
How is your vacation? I'm still selling lemonade. I bought some baseball cards. When you get back, I'll show them to you.

**closing**
Your friend,

**signature**
Benjy

### How to Write a Friendly Letter
1. Write the heading. It contains your address and the date.
2. Write the greeting. Capitalize the first letter of each word.
3. Write a message in the body of the letter. Always indent the first line of the body.
4. Use a closing to end the letter.
5. Sign the letter with your name.

✐ **Practice**

Underline the sentences that might be in a letter that Jason writes to answer Benjy's. Explain each of your choices.

1. Football is my favorite sport. _____

2. My vacation has been fun. _____

3. My brother and I were sick. _____

4. I bought baseball cards, too. _____

Name _____ Date _____

☞ An **invitation** is a letter that asks someone to come somewhere. It has the same five parts as a friendly letter.

| | |
|---|---|
| 3 Church Street | **heading** |
| New London, CT 06320 | |
| May 11, 1999 | |
| | |
| Dear Mr. Cravitz, | **greeting** |
|        I would like to invite you to a special lunch at | **body** |
| Mr. and Mrs. Bunker's house on Saturday, June 2. | |
| The lunch will begin at 1:00 P.M. and end at about 4:00 P.M. | |
|        Your friend, | **closing** |
|        Bethany | **signature** |

---

**How to Write an Invitation**

1. Tell who is invited.
2. Tell what the invitation is for.
3. Tell when to come and when the event will end.
4. Tell where it is.
5. Tell any special information your guest must know.

---

✏ **Practice**

Use the example invitation to answer these questions.

1. Who is invited? _____

2. What is the event? _____

3. Where and when will the event take place? _____

_____

4. At what time will the event begin and end? _____

Name _____  Date _____

☞ In a **thank-you note** you thank someone for something he or she has given you or done for you.

**heading**                3 Nyac Street
                           Wasilla, AK 99654
                           January 11, 1999

**greeting**        Dear Grandmother,

**body**            Thank you so much for giving me the beautiful white skates
                    for my birthday. You helped make this my happiest birthday ever.

**closing**                        Your granddaughter,

**signature**                      Cara

---

### How to Write a Thank-You Note
**1.** Tell what you are thanking the person for.
**2.** If you have been a visitor somewhere, tell why you enjoyed yourself.
**3.** If you received a gift, say how you are using it.
**4.** Include the five parts of a friendly letter.

---

✐ **Practice**
Pretend you are Cara. Write two more sentences to add to the example thank-you note.

_____

_____

_____

_____

_____

Name _____  Date _____

## Address an Envelope

☞ An **envelope** is used to send a letter or a note.

☞ The receiver's **address** goes toward the center. The **return address** goes in the upper left corner.

☞ **Postal abbreviations** are used for state names.

☞ The **ZIP Code** is written after the state abbreviation.

Chester O'Toole
13 Bridge Street
Wasilla, AK 99654                     **return address**

       Joe Canton
       15 Talkeetna Road          **receiver's name and address**
       Nome, AK 99762

### Postal Abbreviations

| | | | | | |
|---|---|---|---|---|---|
| Alabama | AL | Kentucky | KY | North Dakota | ND |
| Alaska | AK | Louisiana | LA | Ohio | OH |
| Arizona | AZ | Maine | ME | Oklahoma | OK |
| Arkansas | AR | Maryland | MD | Oregon | OR |
| California | CA | Massachusetts | MA | Pennsylvania | PA |
| Colorado | CO | Michigan | MI | Rhode Island | RI |
| Connecticut | CT | Minnesota | MN | South Carolina | SC |
| Delaware | DE | Mississippi | MS | South Dakota | SD |
| District of Columbia | DC | Missouri | MO | Tennessee | TN |
| Florida | FL | Montana | MT | Texas | TX |
| Georgia | GA | Nebraska | NE | Utah | UT |
| Hawaii | HI | Nevada | NV | Vermont | VT |
| Idaho | ID | New Hampshire | NH | Virginia | VA |
| Illinois | IL | New Jersey | NJ | Washington | WA |
| Indiana | IN | New Mexico | NM | West Virginia | WV |
| Iowa | IA | New York | NY | Wisconsin | WI |
| Kansas | KS | North Carolina | NC | Wyoming | WY |

### ✐ Practice

Join a partner. Fold a piece of paper in thirds to look like an envelope. Address the envelope. Use your address as the return address and your partner's address as the receiver.

## Journal Writing

☞ In a **journal** a writer keeps a record of daily events. Writers often use their journals for ideas.

September 7, 1999

School started this week. I think that arithmetic is going to be my favorite subject. Today we had to write our own multiplication problems. I didn't know what to write about! Then I looked around the room and got an idea. I saw books on some desks. So I wrote a problem that asked my group to figure out how many textbooks were in the room. Everyone thought my problem was fun to do, so I felt good.

---

### How to Write a Journal
1. Write the date.
2. Write important things that happened that day.
3. Explain why the events are important to you.

---

✎ **Practice**

Write a short journal entry about something that happened to you at school today. Think about why it is important to you.

_____

_____

_____

_____

_____

_____

_____

_____

Name _____ Date _____

## Tell About a Book

☞ In a **book report** a writer gives a summary of the important events in a book. The writer also gives his or her opinion of the book.

**Title**        <u>The King's Drum and Other African Stories</u>

**Author**     Harold Courlander

**Summary**  This book is a collection of tales from Africa. My favorite is "The Fisherman." It's a funny story about a seagull that has questions about the ocean. Some of the answers he gets are very funny.

**Opinion**   I liked this story's humor. I enjoyed this book very much.

---

### How to Write a Book Report

1. Write the title of the book.
2. Give the author's name.
3. Write a summary. Tell the main idea and some interesting details. Do not give away the ending.
4. Give your opinion of the book. Tell whether you liked it.

---

✎ **Practice**

Answer these questions about the example book report.

1. What kind of book is this? _____

_____

2. Who wrote the book? _____

_____

3. Why does the writer of the book report like this book?_____

_____

Name _____ Date _____

## Unit Six Assessment: Paragraphs

✐  Look at the picture. Choose one of the kinds of paragraphs in the box. Circle your choice. Write a paragraph about the picture using the kind of paragraph writing you chose.

Note: Be sure to follow the rules for a good paragraph.
• Indent your first line.
• Write a topic sentence that tells the main idea.
• Write detail sentences that tell more about the main idea.

---

**Kinds of Paragraphs**

**how-to paragraph** (uses *first, next, then,* and *last*)
**comparison paragraph** (tells how things are alike)
**contrast paragraph** (tells how things are different)
**cause-and-effect paragraph** (gives the cause, then explains the effect)
**information paragraph** (tells why things happen)
**definition paragraph** (tells what something means)
**descriptive paragraph** (uses describing words)
**opinion paragraph** (tells your feelings about a topic)
**persuasive paragraph** (tries to convince the reader to agree with writer)

---

_____

_____

_____

_____

_____

_____

_____

_____

Name _____ Date _____

## Write a Paragraph

☞ A **paragraph** is a group of sentences that tells about one main idea. The first line of a paragraph is **indented**. This means the first word is moved in a little from the left margin.

☞ The **topic sentence** expresses the main idea of the paragraph. It tells what all the other sentences in the paragraph are about. The topic sentence is often the first sentence in a paragraph.

☞ The other sentences in a paragraph are **detail sentences**. Detail sentences add information about the topic sentence. They help the audience understand more about the main idea.

Greenland has a very cold climate. This island is located in the northwest Atlantic Ocean near the Arctic Ocean. More than 85 percent of Greenland is covered with an ice sheet, or glacier. This far north the ice does not all melt during the summer. The summer sun causes icebergs to break off the ice sheet and to float down the rivers.

GREENLAND

---

**How to Write a Paragraph**
1. Write a topic sentence that tells the main idea.
2. Indent the first line.
3. Write detail sentences that explain the main idea.

---

✐ **Practice**

Write three detail sentences for this topic sentence.

In the summer you can have lots of fun.

_____

_____

_____

_____

_____

_____

**Paragraph**
**Unit Six: Paragraphs**
Language Arts 4, SV 3890-5

Name _____ Date _____

## The How-To Paragraph

☞ In a **how-to paragraph** a writer explains how to do something.

☞ Detail sentences in a how-to paragraph use **time-order** words to show correct order.

If you want to sell something, you can make signs to put around your neighborhood. You will need large pieces of tagboard, a marker, and some tacks. First, write on your tagboard what you are selling, its price, and your address. Next, put up your signs. Be sure to put your signs where everyone can read them. Finally, place a sign near your home so people know where to find you.

---

### How to Write a How-to Paragraph

1. Write a topic sentence that tells what you are going to explain how to do.
2. Add a detail sentence that lists the materials.
3. Write detail sentences that tell the steps in order.
4. Use time-order words, such as *first, next, then, last,* and *finally,* to show the order of the steps.

---

### ✐ Practice

Number these sentences for a how-to paragraph in the correct order.

_____ You will need six oranges, a bowl, a strainer, water, ice, and a pitcher.

_____ Next, place each half over the bowl and squeeze hard.

_____ Finally, add water and ice cubes, and stir.

_____ Making orangeade is easy if you follow these steps.

_____ First, cut each orange in half.

_____ Then pour the juice through the strainer and into the pitcher.

Name _____ Date _____

## Paragraphs That Compare

☞ In a **comparison paragraph** a writer shows how two people, places, or things are alike.

The folk tale "Half a Kingdom" is like the fairy tale "Snow White" in its kinds of characters, its magic, and its ending. Signy lives in a forest. Snow White lives in a forest, too. In both these stories, a character falls asleep under a magic spell. Prince Lini is put to sleep with a magic fog. Snow White falls asleep when she eats a poisoned apple. Finally, the endings of both stories are also alike. Both Signy and Snow White live happily ever after.

---

**How to Write a Comparison Paragraph**

1. Choose two subjects to compare.
2. Think of three ways your subjects are alike.
3. Write a topic sentence that tells what you are going to compare and how your subjects are alike.
4. Give examples that clearly explain each quality in the detail sentences.
5. Write about each quality in the same order you introduced it in the topic sentence.

---

✐ **Practice**

List the details from the example comparison paragraph that show how the subjects are alike.

_____

_____

_____

_____

_____

_____

_____

**75**

Name _____ Date _____

## Paragraphs That Contrast

☞ In a **contrast paragraph** a writer shows how two or more people or things are different.

The boy was smarter than the witches in the story "The Lost Prince." When the boy found the prince, he remembered to leave a trail so that he could get back out of the cave. Then, when the prince and the boy got to the lake, the witches thought they could catch them. But the boy had hidden a boat in the reeds and was able to escape. When the witches thought they could cast a spell on the boy, he knew that he would be able to resist if he did not look into their eyes. The boy and the prince were able to get back to the castle, and the witches could not stop them!

---

### How to Write a Contrast Paragraph
1. Choose two people, places, or things to contrast.
2. Think of at least two important ways in which your subjects are different.
3. Write a topic sentence that tells what you are going to contrast and how your subjects are different.
4. In the detail sentences, give examples that clearly explain each difference between your subjects.
5. Write about the differences in the same order you introduced them in the topic sentence.

---

✏ **Practice**

List details from the example contrast paragraph that tell how the subjects are different.

_____

_____

_____

_____

_____

_____

Name _____ Date _____

## Cause and Effect

☞ A **cause** is an event that makes something else happen. An **effect** is something
that happens as a result of a cause. In a **cause-and-effect paragraph** a writer first
gives a cause. Then he or she explains what effect or effects happen because of it.

The dog was hungry, so he went looking for a bone. He knew there was none in
his yard, so he began walking up the street. Soon he was
far away from home, and he was not sure where he was!
He had been sniffing the ground, so he did not watch where
he was going. He decided he should use his nose to find his
way back home again. When he got there, his boy was so happy to see him that he
gave the dog a big bone!

---

### How to Write a Cause-and-Effect Paragraph
1. Write a topic sentence that tells what happened.
2. Tell the effects of what happened in the detail sentences.
3. Write the detail sentences in the order in which the effects happened.

---

✏ **Practice**

Finish this chart. Use the example cause-and-effect paragraph.

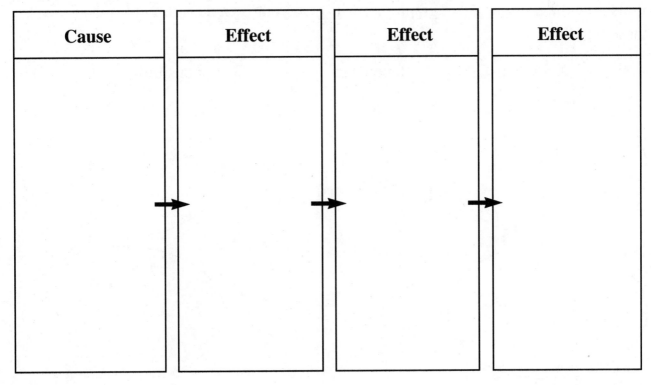

| Cause | Effect | Effect | Effect |
|-------|--------|--------|--------|
|       |        |        |        |

Name _____   Date _____

## Paragraphs That Define

☞ In a **definition paragraph** a writer answers the question, "What is it?" The answer can be about an object, a word, or an idea. Then the definition is expanded with examples. Sometimes the writer's feelings about the topic are also included.

A work song such as "The Erie Canal" is more than just a tune and some words. It is a part of our history. Long ago, a work song was a way for workers to express themselves as they built bridges or dug canals. The beats of the songs matched the rhythms of the body's movements as workers lifted, dug, or hammered. The songs helped pass the time as workers built many of the bridges and roads we still use today.

---

**How to Write a Definition Paragraph**
1. Choose a word or idea to explain.
2. Tell what you will define in the topic sentence.
3. Use clear examples to explain your definition.
4. Use exact words to make your examples clear.

---

✐ **Practice**

Finish the diagram for a paragraph that will give your own definition of one of these words.

**1.** strength          **2.** courage          **3.** responsibility

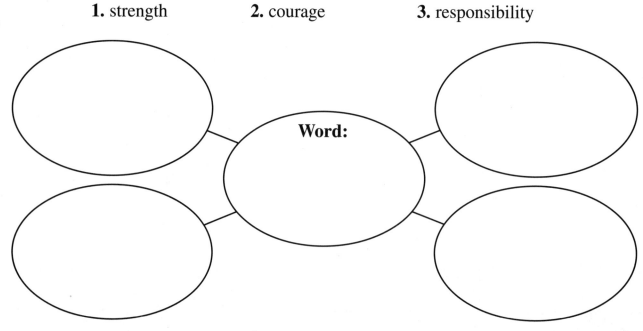

Word:

**Definition Paragraph**
**Unit Six: Paragraphs**
Language Arts 4, SV 3890-5

## Paragraphs That Describe

☞ In a **descriptive paragraph** a writer describes a person, place, object, or event. The paragraph should let the audience *see, feel, hear,* and sometimes *taste* or *smell* what is being described.

The girl thought her new doll was beautiful. It had a face that had been painted with bright colors. Its eyes looked lifelike. The clothes of the doll were finely stitched. There were beautiful buttons on the jacket, and soft lace was sewn around the hem of the dress. Her shoes were as soft as butter to touch.

---

**How to Write a Descriptive Paragraph**

1. Write a topic sentence telling what the paragraph is about.
2. Add detail sentences that give exact information about your topic.
3. Use colorful and lively words to describe the topic. Make an exact picture for your audience with the words you choose.

---

✏ **Practice**

Add descriptive words to this paragraph to make it clearer and more interesting to read.

The girl was worried about her doll. Her **1)**_____ brother had

wanted to play with the doll. The girl had told him that the doll was too

**2)**_____ to play with. Now the girl was in school, away from her

**3)**_____ doll. She had tried to put the doll in a **4)**_____

place. But her brother was very **5)**_____ and **6)**_____.

The girl felt **7)**_____ thinking of what could happen if her brother

found the doll!

Name _____ Date _____

☞ In an **opinion paragraph** a writer tells his or her feelings about a topic. The topic sentence tells the writer's opinion. The detail sentences explain why the writer feels as he or she does.

   I think pigs deserve much more respect from people than they get. Many people think that pigs are ugly, dirty, and not very smart. First of all, pigs are not ugly. Pigs come in many colors and markings. Pigs are not dirty, either. They really keep themselves cleaner than most other farm animals. Pigs are also smart. They know how to find food underground by sniffing with their noses.

---

**How to Write an Opinion Paragraph**

**1.** Write a topic sentence that tells your opinion.

**2.** Remember your audience as you write.

**3.** Tell about your opinion in the detail sentences.

**4.** Give examples that show why you feel as you do.

---

✐ **Practice**

Finish this chart using the example opinion paragraph.

**Opinion:** _____

**Reason 1:** _____

   **Example:** _____

**Reason 2:** _____

   **Example:** _____

**Reason 3:** _____

   **Example:** _____

Name _____ Date _____

## The Power of Persuasion

☞ In a **persuasive paragraph** a writer tries to convince the audience to agree with his or her opinion on a topic.

I think students should vote for the lioness as the symbol of our new school. The lioness is intelligent and carries herself with pride. Aren't intelligence and pride in ourselves the qualities we students want to show? Most of all, I think the lioness brings out a feeling of respect in people. People do not usually take advantage of a lioness. By voting for the lioness, we will choose a symbol of intelligence, pride, and respect.

---

### How to Write a Persuasive Paragraph

1. Write a topic sentence that tells the issue and your opinion about it.
2. Give at least three reasons that will convince your audience to agree with you. Include these reasons in the detail sentences.
3. Explain each reason with one or more examples.
4. Save your strongest reason for last.

---

✎ **Practice**

Complete this chart using details from the example persuasive paragraph.

| |
|---|
| **Topic:** |
| **Audience:** |
| **Reasons:** |

© Steck-Vaughn Company

Persuasive Paragraph
Unit Six: Paragraphs
Language Arts 4, SV 3890-5

Name _____ Date _____

## Unit Seven Assessment: Resource Materials and Research

✏ Use the example book pages to answer the questions.

| A Number of Stories | Contents |
|---|---|
| by Lisa Newton<br><br>Brandywine Arts, Inc.<br>Chicago, Illinois | Adding It Up . . . . . . . . 1<br>Magic Numbers . . . . . 10<br>Time Tells All . . . . . . 17<br>Triple Trouble . . . . . . 42<br>Millions of Dimes . . . 58 |

1. What is the title of the book? _____

2. On what page is "Triple Trouble"?_____

3. Who is the publisher of the book? _____

✏ Tell if each selection is *fiction, nonfiction, biography,* or *reference.*

4. Information Please Almanac _____

5. The Patriotic Turkey _____

6. Abe Lincoln Grows Up _____

7. Four Days in July (true story of the signing of the Declaration of Independence)

_____

✏ Use the example dictionary page to answer these questions.

> **club** detector
>
> **club** [klub] *n., v.* **clubbed, clubbing 1** *n.* Heavy wooden stick for use as a weapon, generally thicker at one end. **2** *n.* A stick or bat used to hit a ball: a golf *club.* **3** *n.* A figure like this: ♣ **4** *n.* A playing card of the suit marked with black club figures. **5** *n.* A group of people organized for enjoyment of some purpose: a social *club.*
>
> **clue** [kloo] *n.* A hint or piece of evidence, helpful in solving a problem or mystery.
>
> **D**
> **de·tec·tive** [di·tek'tiv] **1** *n.* A person, often a police officer, whose work is to investigate crimes, find out hidden information, and watch suspected persons. **2** *adj.* Of, for, or about detectives and their work: a *detective* story.

8. What are the guide words on this page? _____

9. Would the word *cluck* be on this page? _____

✏ Use an encyclopedia to find information on a place that you would like to visit. Take notes, and then use the information you find to write a paragraph about the place. Use the back of this paper or another piece of paper for your work.

Name _____ Date _____

## Book Parts

☞ The **title page** tells the title of a book. It gives the name of the author. It also tells the name of the publishing company and its location.

☞ The **table of contents** comes after the title page. It lists the titles of the chapters, units, stories, or poems in the book. It also lists the pages on which they begin. Everything in the book is listed in the order in which it appears.

| A Number of Stories |
| :---: |
| by |
| Lisa Newton |
| |
| Brandywine Arts, Inc. |
| Chicago, Illinois |

**title page**

| Contents |
| :--- |
| Adding It Up . . . . . . . 1 |
| Magic Numbers . . . . . 10 |
| Time Tells All . . . . . . 17 |
| Triple Trouble . . . . . . 42 |
| Millions of Dimes . . . 58 |

**table of contents**

✏ **Practice**

**A.** Tell whether this information would be found on the *title page* or in the *table of contents*.

**1.** the author of the book _____

**2.** the title of the book _____

**3.** the name of each story _____

**4.** the page where a story is found _____

**5.** the publisher of the book _____

**6.** the location of the publisher _____

**B.** Answer these questions about the example pages.

**7.** How do you know Lisa Newton's stories are in the book? _____

**8.** On what page does the story "Triple Trouble" begin? _____

**9.** What story begins on page 58? _____

**Parts of a Book**
**Unit Seven: Resource Materials and Research**
Language Arts 4, SV 3890-5

Name _____ Date _____

## Finding Information

☞ A **glossary** is like a small dictionary in the back of a book. It gives the meanings for words in the book that the reader may not know. The meanings define the words only in the way they are used in the book. The words are listed in alphabetical order.

☞ An **index** is a list of all the topics in a book. The index lists the page number or numbers on which each topic appears. It is arranged in alphabetical order.

| | |
|---|---|
| **an•swer** {an´sər} *n*. A solution to an arithmetic problem. <br> **a•rith•me•tic** {ə•rith´mə•tik} <br> *n*. A kind of mathematics that deals with numbers. <br> **dou•ble** {dub´əl} *v*. To make or become twice as much. | Subtraction <br>    fractions, 58–60, 119 <br>    whole numbers, 15, 17–20 <br> Word problems <br>    addition, 2–4, 39 <br>    division, 40–45, 68 <br>    multiplication, 25–33, 62 <br>    subtraction, 19–20, 60 |
| **glossary** | **index** |

✐ **Practice**

Answer these questions. Tell if you used the example *glossary* or *index* to find the answer.

1. What word means "to make or become twice as much"?

_____

2. On which pages could you find multiplication word problems?

_____

3. On what page would you first find facts about fractions?

_____

4. What is the definition of *answer*?

_____

© Steck-Vaughn Company

**Parts of a Book** <br> **Unit Seven: Resource Materials and Research** <br> Language Arts 4, SV 3890-5

Name _____ Date _____

## Kinds of Books

☞ The library has different kinds of books.

☞ **Fiction** books are stories that are all or partly imaginary.
<u>The Patriotic Turkey</u>

☞ **Nonfiction** books tell facts about real people, things, or events.
<u>American State Flags</u>

☞ A **biography** is a nonfiction book that tells about the life of a real person.
<u>America's Paul Revere</u>

☞ **Reference books** are nonfiction books that contain facts about many different topics. The encyclopedia, atlas, and dictionary are reference books.
<u>A Dictionary of American Trivia</u>

✏ **Practice**
Read the list of books. Tell if each book is *fiction, nonfiction, biography,* or *reference.* The words in ( ) will help you decide about some books.

1. <u>Information Please Almanac</u> _____

2. <u>Four Days in July</u> (true events of the signing of the

   Declaration of Independence) _____

3. <u>The Courage of Sarah Noble</u> (a made-up story of a girl's life in the

   colonial Connecticut wilderness) _____

4. <u>Abe Lincoln Grows Up</u> _____

5. <u>Who's Who in America</u> _____

6. <u>Drums</u> (a made-up story of the American Revolution) _____

© Steck-Vaughn Company

**Kinds of Books**
**Unit Seven: Resource Materials and Research**
Language Arts 4, SV 3890-5

Name _____ Date _____

## Skimming It

☞ **Skimming** is a quick reading method. When you skim a page in a book, you note its general subject, its divisions, and its major headings.

✏ **Practice**

Skim these paragraphs and answer the questions below.

---

**Staying Healthy**

Here is how to keep yourself strong and healthy. It is important to eat well-balanced meals and exercise often. You must also get plenty of rest and see a doctor for regular checkups.

**Community Health Workers**

Many other people besides doctors work to keep you well. These people are health workers. They include nurses, dentists and dental workers, hospital workers, and food and water inspectors. These people all work hard to take care of the health of people in the community.

---

**1.** By looking at the page quickly, how can you predict what it will be about?

_____

**2.** What are the two most important steps for staying healthy?

_____

**3.** What is the main idea for the first paragraph?

_____

**4.** What is the main idea for the second paragraph?

_____

**5.** Are doctors the only health workers who help you stay healthy?

_____ Why do you think as you do? _____

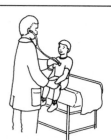

_____

Name _____ Date _____

## Scanning It

☞ **Scanning** is a quick reading method. When you scan a page, you look for key words.

✏ **Practice**

Scan the passage to find the answers to the questions below.

---

### Folk Tales and Fairy Tales

Folk tales and fairy tales are two different kinds of stories. A folk tale tells about the legends and customs of real people. Sometimes America's history is told through the adventures of a folk hero, such as Pecos Bill. However, a fairy tale often takes place in a world of make-believe. "Jack and the Beanstalk," with its giant's castle, is one example of this. A character in a fairy tale is often imaginary and sometimes has magical powers. A fairy-tale princess, like Cinderella, has a fairy godmother to grant wishes magically. Even though the two kinds of stories are different, they both always have a happy ending.

---

1. Is "Jack and the Beanstalk" a folk tale or a fairy tale? _____

2. What is the purpose of a folk tale? _____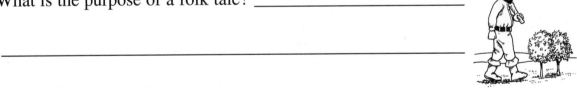

_____

3. Name a fairy-tale princess. _____

4. Where do most fairy tales take place? _____

5. What are folk characters sometimes based on? _____

6. Which kind of story has imaginary creatures? _____

7. What kind of ending do folk tales and fairy tales have? _____

_____

Name _____  Date _____

☞ The order of letters from **A** to **Z** is called **alphabetical order**. Words in a dictionary are listed in alphabetical order. These words are in alphabetical order.

      club      clue      crime      dentist      detective

☞ There are two **guide words** at the top of every dictionary page. The word on the left is the first word on the page. The word on the right is the last word on the page. All other words on the page are in alphabetical order between the guide words.

☞ Each word that is defined in the dictionary is an **entry word**. An entry word usually appears in dark print.

---

club                                       **detector**

**club** [klub] *n., v.* **clubbed, clubbing 1** *n.* Heavy wooden stick for use as a weapon, generally thicker at one end. **2** *n.* A stick or bat used to hit a ball: a golf *club*. **3** *n.* A figure like this: ♣ **4** *n.* A playing card of the suit marked with black club figures. **5** *n.* A group of people organized for enjoyment of some purpose: a social *club*.

**clue** [kloo] *n.* A hint or piece of evidence, helpful in solving a problem or mystery.

**D**

**de·tec·tive** [di·tek′tiv] **1** *n.* A person, often a police officer, whose work is to investigate crimes, find out hidden information, and watch suspected persons. **2** *adj.* Of, for, or about detectives and their work: a *detective* story.

---

✏ **Practice**

Use the example dictionary page to answer these questions.

**1.** What are the guide words on this page? _____

**2.** Could the word *cloth* appear on this page?_____ Why or why not?

    _____

**3.** What is the alphabetical order of these words: *doctor, crime, case, chair*?

    _____

Name _____ Date _____

## Using the Dictionary

☞ An **entry** is all the information about an entry word.

☞ The **part of speech** tells if a word is a noun, a verb, or some other part of speech. The parts of speech in a dictionary are usually abbreviated in this way.

| noun–n. | verb–v. | adjective–adj. |
| adverb–adv. | pronoun–pron. | |

☞ A **definition** is the meaning of a word. Many words have more than one definition. Each definition is numbered.

☞ A definition is often followed by an **example sentence** that shows how to use the word.

> **mys·ter·y** [mis′tər·ē] *n., pl.* **mys·ter·ies**
> **1** Something that is not known, understood, or explained.  **2** Anything, as an action, that arouses curiosity because it is not understood or explained.  **3** Something, as a story or play, about such an action: "The Case of the Missing Roller Skates" is a *mystery*.  **4** A quality of secrecy.

✐ **Practice**
Use the example dictionary entry to answer the following questions.

1. What part of speech is the entry word? _____

2. How many definitions are given for the entry word? _____

3. For which definition is there an example sentence? _____

4. Which definition of *mystery* is used in this sentence?

   Her sudden change in behavior was a complete mystery to all of us.

   _____

5. What information is given right after the part of speech of the entry word?

   _____

**Dictionary**
**Unit Seven: Resource Materials and Research**
Language Arts 4, SV 3890-5

Name _____ Date _____

## The Way to Say It

☞ A **syllable** is a word part that has only one vowel sound. Each entry word in the dictionary is divided into syllables.

☞ A **pronunciation** follows each entry word. It shows how to say the word. It also shows the number of syllables in the word.

☞ The **pronunciation key** lists the symbol for each sound. It also gives a familiar word in which the sound is heard. A pronunciation key usually appears on every other page of the dictionary.

| a | add | i | it | o͞o | took | oi | oil |
|---|-----|---|-----|-----|------|----|-----|
| ā | ace | ī | ice | ōō | pool | ou | pout |
| â | care | o | odd | u | up | ng | ring |
| ä | palm | ō | open | û | burn | th | thin |
| e | end | ô | order | yōō | fuse | th | this |
| ē | equal | | | | | zh | vision |

ə = { a in *above*   e in *sicken*   i in *possible*
      o in *melon*   u in *circus* }

## ✏ Practice

Read each pronunciation. Choose the word that matches the pronunciation. Tell how many syllables are in the word.

1. pär´kə       party        parka        _____

2. snō          snow         sun          _____

3. mə•shēn´     matching     machine      _____

4. kar´ə•bōo    caribou      carbon       _____

5. fä´thər      feather      father       _____

6. sur•prīz     surplus      surprise     _____

7. līt          light        let          _____

8. (h)wāl       wall         whale        _____

Name _____ Date _____

## Reference Books

☞ An **encyclopedia** is a set of
books that contains information
on many subjects. Each book in a
set is called a **volume**. Subjects
are arranged in alphabetical order

| A | B | C–D | E–F | G–H I | J–K L | M | N–O | P–Q | R–S | T–U V | W–X Y–Z |
|---|---|-----|-----|-------|-------|---|-----|-----|-----|-------|---------|
| 1 | 2 | 3   | 4   | 5     | 6     | 7 | 8   | 9   | 10  | 11    | 12      |

in each volume. Volumes are also arranged in alphabetical order.

☞ Some encyclopedias have a separate **index**. The index lists the number of the
volume or volumes in which information about a subject can be found.

✎ **Practice**

A. Use the example encyclopedia to find the number of the volume in which you
would find each of these subjects.

1. Baffin Bay          _____

2. Arctic Circle       _____

3. penguins            _____

4. fur                 _____

5. North Pole          _____

6. kayaks              _____

7. Eskimos             _____

8. whales              _____

9. seals               _____

10. ice                _____

B. Underline the word or words you would use to find the following information in
an encyclopedia.

11. the capital of Greenland

12. animals of the Arctic

13. climate at the South Pole

14. expeditions of Robert E. Peary

15. the average daily temperature in Alaska

**Encyclopedia**
**Unit Seven: Resource Materials and Research**
Language Arts 4, SV 3890-5

Name _____ Date _____

## Finding Your Way

☞ An **atlas** is a book of maps.

☞ A **legend** lists and explains the symbols on a map.

☞ The **direction symbol,** or **compass rose,** tells you which way is north, south, east, or west on the map.

☞ The **distance scale** shows the distance on the map.

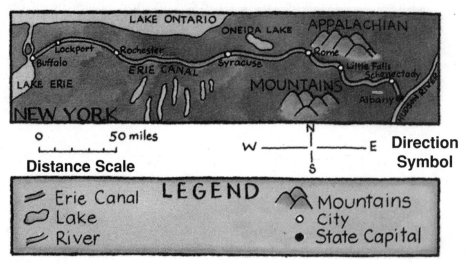

### ✐ **Practice**

Use the map to answer the following questions.

1. Which two bodies of water are connected by the Erie Canal? _____

   _____

2. Which two cities are at the ends of the canal? _____

3. In what direction must you travel to get from Albany to Buffalo? _____

   _____

4. What is the capital of New York state? _____

   How do you know? _____

5. About how far is it from Albany to Buffalo? _____

6. In what two directions from the Erie Canal do the Appalachian Mountains lie?

7. What lake is between Syracuse and Rome? _____

Name _____  Date _____

## The Card Catalog

☞ A **card catalog** is a set of cards that lists every book in the library. The cards in the card catalog are in alphabetical order. The cards are usually kept in drawers. On the outside of the drawers are guide letters. These letters tell the first letter on the cards in that drawer. There are three kinds of cards in the library.

☞ The **title card** lists the title of the book first.

☞ The **author card** lists the author's last name first.

☞ The **subject card** lists the subject of the book first. Use subject cards when you are looking for a book on a topic but do not know the title or author.

☞ Many libraries now have their card catalog on computer.

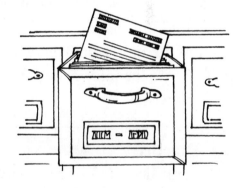

| 659.1 | **ADVERTISING** |
| C | **Capler, John** |
| | How to make your advertising make money/John Capler, Englewood Cliffs, NJ: Prentice-Hall, 1983 |

✐ **Practice**

Use the example card to answer the following questions.

1. What is the title of the book?_____

2. Under which subject would you find this book? _____

3. Which type of card would tell you this information? _____

4. How could you find this book in the library if you did not know its author

   but did know its title?_____

5. In what state was this book published? _____

6. What is the publisher's name? _____

7. What does the date 1983 tell you?_____

Name _____   Date _____

## Taking Notes

☞ A good writer takes notes to remember the facts he or she finds when doing research for a report.

> <u>Royal Symbols</u> by Crystal Wong, pages 15-16
> Who has used the dragon as a symbol?
> emperors of China
> kings of England

---

**How to Take Notes**

1. Write a question. Then find a book to answer your question.
2. List the title of the book, the author, and the page numbers on which you find information.
3. Write only facts you want to include in your report.
4. Write the information in your own words. Write sentences or short groups of words.

---

✐ **Practice**

The items listed below are from the same pages of the book used for the example notes above. On two index cards or on another piece of paper, write notes that answer each of the questions below. Model your answers on the example notes above.

What things did the dragon stand for?
What did the dragon look like?

1. symbol of kindness
2. beast with long tail
3. symbol of fear
4. symbol of power
5. similar to a dinosaur

Name _____ Date _____

## Writing an Outline

☞ A writer uses an **outline** to organize the information he or she has gathered for a research report.

### Royal Dragons

  I.  Symbol of Chinese royalty
     A.  Powerful, kind beast
     B.  Blessed the people
 II.  Symbol used by English kings
     A.  Frightening beast
     B.  Represented protection

### How to Make an Outline
**1.** Write a title that tells the subject of your report.
**2.** Write each main topic. Use a Roman numeral and a period.
**3.** Write subtopics under each main topic. Use a capital letter followed by a period for each subtopic.

### ✐ Practice
On the back of this paper or on another piece of paper, organize and write these items in correct outline form.

**1.** <u>The Falcon</u>
Falcon was symbol of Egyptian King Ramses II
god of the sky
protected the king

**2.** <u>The Crane</u>
Crane is symbol used in Japan
stands for good luck
used in folk tales

Name _____ Date _____

## Writing a Rough Draft

☞ A writer quickly puts all of his or her ideas on paper in a **rough draft**.

---

**How to Write a Rough Draft**

1. Read over your notes and your outline.
2. Follow your notes and outline to make a rough draft.
3. Write one paragraph for each Roman numeral in your outline.
4. Write your rough draft quickly.
5. Read over your rough draft. Makes notes on changes you want to make.

---

✏ **Practice**

Choose one of the outlines below. Write a rough draft of a paragraph for this outline. Include one topic sentence and two detail sentences. Remember to write quickly.

1.       Bears as Indian Symbols

   I. Bear symbolized protection to some Indians
      A. Bear masks worn to protect against enemies
      B. Bears in totem poles protected homes

2.       Bears as Symbols of Sports Teams

   I. Bear used as symbol in baseball and football
      A. Football–Chicago Bears
      B. Baseball–Chicago Cubs

_____

_____

_____

_____

_____

_____

_____

_____

Name _____ Date _____

☞ When a writer makes all the changes in the rough draft, he or she writes the final copy of the **research report**.

### Royal Dragons

Many Chinese emperors used a dragon to represent the royal family. The dragon was considered a powerful, kind creature in Chinese myths. People thought the dragon brought them rain, good crops, and good fortune.

Kings of England also chose the dragon for their symbol. They thought the dragon was a frightening beast that would scare the enemy. Long ago, battle shields of the English army had dragons on them. It was believed that a dragon would protect the carriers of the shields.

---

### How to Write a Research Report
1. Write the title of your report.
2. Write the report from your rough draft and your notes.
3. Makes all changes you marked on your rough draft.
4. Indent the first sentence of each paragraph.

---

✐ **Practice**

Read the example research report on this page. Then choose a topic that interests you and write your own report. Remember to take notes, make an outline, write a rough draft, and then write your report. Save all your notes to turn in with your report. Your report should be at least two paragraphs long and should have a title.

Name _____ Date _____

## Unit Eight Assessment: Reading Comprehension

Read the story, then answer the questions.

I was watching my neighbor's dog, Phil, the other day, and he got away. The neighbor said I should always keep a leash on Phil, but Phil was being so good, I didn't think he would run. Boy, was I wrong! Phil saw a cat, and he was off in a flash. I must have looked for him for an hour. I felt awful that I had let my neighbor down. I wished I could just snap my fingers and Phil would appear next to me. As it turned out, Phil came back on his own. He had rolled in something that smelled bad, but he was back! I was so happy to see him, I didn't even mind getting soaked while I gave him a bath.

1. To whom did Phil belong? _____

2. Why did Phil run away? _____

3. Tell something in the story that could not really happen. _____

_____

4. Tell something in the story that could have happened. _____

_____

5. What did the writer do after Phil came back? _____

_____

6. Do you think the writer should have let Phil off his leash? _____

_____

7. Why or why not? _____

_____

8. If you were Phil's owner, would you let the writer watch Phil again? _____

Why or why not? _____

## Drawing Conclusions

### The Best Bird

Everyone was planning to come to the class party as a different kind of bird. Arthur wanted to come as some special bird that is very fierce and beautiful. Most of the fierce and beautiful birds were already taken. Bruce was coming as an eagle. Beatrice would be a falcon. Peter would be a hawk. So, Arthur had to think of something else.

Arthur was considering coming as a blue jay. Bruce said that blue jays are mean and sassy but not fierce. "Crows sound fierce sometimes," Beatrice said.

"Why don't you come as a whooping crane?" Peter said. "Whooping cranes are nearly extinct, so you wouldn't even have to show up."

Willa was coming as a dove, so she felt that it was her job to make peace. "I have an idea," she whispered to Arthur.

At the party, Bruce and Peter waited to see what bird Arthur would be. Peter was teasing Bruce about looking more like a parrot than an eagle. Then Arthur came in, and everyone's eyes were on his beautiful purple and white costume. He had come as the make-believe bird, the phoenix.

"In many old stories," Willa explained, "the phoenix stands for beauty, excellence, and long life."

"I wish I'd thought of that," Peter said.

*Go on to the next page.*

## Drawing Conclusions, p. 2

1. Arthur probably wanted to come as a special bird because
   a. he didn't care what he looked like at the party.
   b. he wanted to make a big hit at the party.
   c. he wanted to look just like his friend Peter.
   d. he thought the party was not a good idea.

2. Peter probably told Arthur to come as a whooping crane because
   a. he didn't want Arthur to come to the party.
   b. he wanted Arthur to look silly.
   c. he thought he was being funny.
   d. he thought he was better than Arthur.

3. Willa is probably the kind of girl who
   a. tries to help her friends.
   b. makes fun of her friends.
   c. wants everything to go her way.
   d. wants to have the only good costume.

4. When Arthur came as a phoenix, everyone was probably
   a. bored.
   b. angry.
   c. surprised.
   d. embarrassed.

5. At the end of the story, how does Arthur probably feel toward Willa?
   a. confused
   b. irritated
   c. grateful
   d. concerned

## Comparing and Contrasting

### Good Friends

After Kristin and her mom had moved to Maine from the town in Florida where they had always lived, she missed her friend, Nicky. Kristin and Nicky had promised to write to each other, but neither girl was sure that they would stick to their agreement.

After a year, though, they were still writing. In each letter, Nicky told Kristin news about the people and places in the town where they had both grown up. Kristin enjoyed her new home, but reading Nicky's letters made her long to see familiar people and places.

Kristin's letters to Nicky were quite different. They told about exciting new experiences. They told of snow, sleds, skis, snowmobiles, and other winter things that were new to Kristin. Reading Kristin's letters made Nicky want to visit her badly.

Kristin surprised Nicky with a phone call one day to tell her about an idea that her mother had. She invited Nicky to visit her new home during winter vacation. She also asked if Nicky's family would let her stay with them for a few weeks in the summer.

Nicky asked her parents about what Kristin had suggested. They said it would be fine, but they wanted her to help pay for her trip by earning some of the money herself. Nicky agreed, but when she sat down to figure out her plans, she was not able to think of any ideas to earn money. She wrote to Kristin asking for ideas.

*Go on to the next page.*

Name _____ Date _____

## Comparing and Contrasting, p. 2

✏ Answer each question about the story.

1. Name two ways in which Kristin's new home is different from her old one.

    **a.** _____

    **b.** _____

2. Name two things that Kristin can do in Maine that she could not do in Florida.

    **a.** _____

    **b.** _____

3. Name two ways in which Nicky and Kristin are alike.

    **a.** _____

    **b.** _____

4. Why might Nicky want to visit Kristin in Maine?

    _____

    _____

5. Why might Kristin want to visit Nicky in Florida?

    _____

    _____

Comparing and Contrasting
Unit Eight: Reading Comprehension
Language Arts 4, SV 3890-5

Name _____ Date _____

## Good Guy

Bobby guessed that they were going on a Sunday drive, so when they pulled into Top Breed Kennels, he was surprised. "We promised you a dog," his mother said, "and today you can pick one out."

The kennel sold poodle and collie puppies, and as Bobby walked down the aisle between the pens with the beautiful pups, he wanted them all. The dogs yipped and came to the screen to lick his fingers. Bobby said that picking one dog would be like freeing it, but the man who sold the dogs said, "All of these pups will find homes. Today, people want pure-blooded dogs. These dogs will all have new homes within weeks."

Bobby's father suggested that they look at other dogs before Bobby made his choice, so they visited other kennels. Bobby saw Airedales, cocker spaniels, and so many kinds of dogs that he felt confused. The last stop had a sign reading "County Humane Society."

Inside, a full-grown dog with long ears and uneven dark spots stood, slowly wagging its stubby tail and watching with big, brown eyes as Bobby looked in the pens. "I hope someone picks him soon," the lady on duty said. "He's such a nice dog. He's a mongrel, but such a good guy; and we can't keep him much longer."

Outside, the dog wiggled with glee as Bobby led him on a leash to the car. "Come on, Good Guy," Bobby said, "we're going to show you your new home."

*Go on to the next page.*

Name _____  Date _____

✐  Think about the story you read. Look at the diagram below. There are some ways that Good Guy and the other dogs that Bobby sees are alike. There are some ways that they are different. Add two items to each circle.

Remember that where the circles overlap shows how Good Guy and the other dogs are alike.

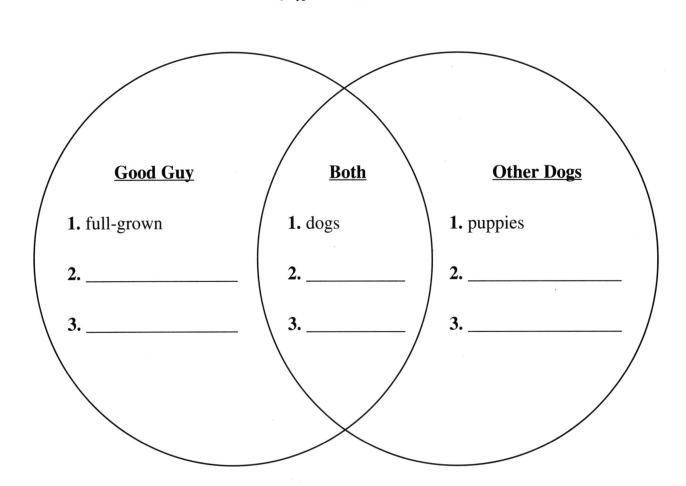

**Good Guy**

1. full-grown

2. _____

3. _____

**Both**

1. dogs

2. _____

3. _____

**Other Dogs**

1. puppies

2. _____

3. _____

## Identifying Important Details

### Ghost Stories

In the darkness Pepper couldn't see his friends sitting around him in Betty's backyard as he made up his story. Meg had just finished one about Charlotte, an English girl who was lost and came to a big, dingy castle. Charlotte went from room to room following strange noises made by squeaking shutters or broken curtain rods scraping against windows.

Pepper decided to continue Meg's story. "Charlotte heard moans from below," he said. "She started down some dark stone stairs leading to an old, smelly cellar. She put her hand on the wall to feel her way, and it was wet and cold and sticky."

The story must have scared Betty's black cat, Andy. He got up to go to the front yard and brushed against Meg's leg. "Agghhh! Get out of here!" Meg cried.

"At the bottom of the stairs," Pepper continued, "Charlotte turned a corner toward a flickering light. Her blood turned ice cold when she saw..."

"Yeeee-ike! Help! Help!" someone screamed from the front of the house. The children ran out front, almost expecting to find poor Charlotte. There stood Mrs. Winters, a neighbor, pointing to a big shopping bag she had dropped on the sidewalk. "Some creature jumped into my bag," she shrieked. Two yellow eyes slowly peeped up from inside the bag.

"It's only Andy," Betty said.

*Go on to the next page.*

Name _____ Date _____

✏ Answer each question about the story. Circle the letter in front of the correct answer.

1. Pepper and his friends are
   a. lost somewhere in England.
   b. making up spooky stories.
   c. trapped in a smelly cellar.
   d. looking for Betty's cat.

2. The person who is in the castle is
   a. Betty.
   b. Andy.
   c. Meg.
   d. Charlotte.

3. Meg is frightened when she
   a. feels the cat brush her leg.
   b. hears creaking shutters.
   c. comes to the bottom of the stairs.
   d. sees that Andy is in the bag.

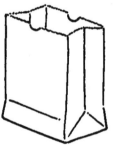

4. Mrs. Winters screams because
   a. the stories frighten her.
   b. she is alone in the castle.
   c. the cat jumps into her bag.
   d. the children frighten her.

5. When the children run out front, they expect to see
   a. Charlotte.
   b. Mrs. Winters.
   c. Pepper.
   d. Andy.

**Sequencing**

## Sleepy Head

Maria was very tired after the visit to Uncle Ned's. As she rode home in the car with her mother, she could barely keep her eyes open.

"Watch out!" Maria called out all at once, sitting up straight in the seat. Maria thought she had seen Paul Bunyan's ox standing by the road, ready to cross. Before she could explain to her mother, their car had passed the ox, which was really just some big mailboxes on posts.

Maria knew that her sleepy eyes were playing tricks on her, but they fooled her again. "Oh, oh!" she sighed when she saw an ambulance stop on the road ahead of them. Then the red light turned green. It was only a traffic light and some shadows on the road.

"You certainly are jumpy tonight," Mother said. "Why don't I stop so you can get in the back seat and sleep?"

When Mother stopped the car, Maria climbed into the back seat, put on her seatbelt, and tried to get comfortable. She closed her weary eyes, but she couldn't get to sleep. She kept thinking that it had begun to storm. The lights from big trucks were flashing into the back seat like lightning.

"It's odd," Maria yawned, "how a person can get too tired to go to sleep anywhere but in her own bed."

*Go on to the next page.*

Name _____ Date _____

**Sequencing, p. 2**

✏ Answer each question about the story. Circle the letter in front of the correct answer.

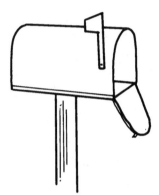

1.  What happened just after Maria thought she saw Paul Bunyan's ox?
    a.  Lights from a big truck flashed in her eyes.
    b.  She went to visit her Uncle Ned.
    c.  The car passed some big mailboxes.
    d.  Maria saw an ambulance.

2.  What happened first in the story?
    a.  Maria and her mother visited Maria's Uncle Ned.
    b.  Maria felt very tired in the car.
    c.  Maria went to bed.
    d.  Maria went to sleep in the car.

3.  What happened after Maria got into the back seat?
    a.  She thought she saw Paul Bunyan's ox.
    b.  She got into her own bed.
    c.  She fell asleep.
    d.  She thought it had begun to storm.

4.  What happened just before the car passed a traffic light and some shadows?
    a.  The car passed the mailboxes.
    b.  Maria called, "Watch out!"
    c.  Maria thought she saw an ambulance.
    d.  It began to storm.

5.  What happened just after Maria's mother stopped the car?
    a.  Maria got into the back seat.
    b.  Maria put on her seatbelt.
    c.  Maria and her mother rode to Uncle Ned's house.
    d.  Maria and her mother got something to eat.

Name _____     Date _____

## Identifying Cause and Effect

### The Train in Spain

Alex and his father went by jet to Spain. When they got there, they decided to travel on the train, which most people take to get from one town to another. Alex wanted to meet the people.

The train was nearly empty when Alex and his father boarded to go 100 kilometers to the next big city. There were many empty wooden seats.

The train creaked along very slowly, stopping at every little town. More and more people got on board. It was Sunday, and Alex could hear the excited voices of people crowding the platform near the tracks as the train approached each station.

The passengers carried small children, wicker luggage, baskets of food, and even some live chickens. People soon filled all the aisles, and some had to climb in and out of the train's open windows when it came to their stations.

Everyone was very friendly. People shared their lunches with

Alex and his father, who joined in singing jolly songs. Alex had to shout to answer many questions about America. The trip took over six hours, and it was a hoarse and tired boy who bid good-bye to all his new friends.

"That was a wonderful trip," Alex told his father, "and I want to travel with the people of Spain again before we leave. But let's rent a car for a while."

*Go on to the next page.*

Name _____ Date _____

## Identifying Cause and Effect, p. 2

✏️ Finish each sentence about the story. Circle the *cause* in each sentence. Underline the *effect*.

1. Alex and his father decided to travel on the train because _____

   _____

2. Because the aisles were full of people, _____

   _____

3. Alex had to shout to answer people's questions because _____

   _____

4. Because the trip was long and Alex had shouted so much, _____

   _____

5. Alex wanted to rent a car for a while because _____

   _____

Name _____ Date _____

| Making Judgments |

### Cold Hands, Warm Heart

Quinn was shopping in the department store when he saw the woman shaking her finger at the little boy. "He must have done something really bad," Quinn thought, moving down the aisle to hear what she was saying.

"This is the last pair of gloves I'm going to buy you this winter!" the woman said firmly, shaking her finger on one hand and a pair of gloves in the other. "I mean it! If you lose this pair, you can just go around with your hands in your pockets the rest of the winter!"

"Boy, she's really mean," Quinn thought, glaring at the boy's mother.

"What would you do?" the woman almost shouted at Quinn. "This is the third pair of gloves I've had to buy for him this winter! He had each pair a few days and then came home without them! He has to learn to respect things and take good care of them."

"Makes sense to me," Quinn said; and to tell the truth it did, now that she had explained. "How come you're always losing your gloves?" he asked the boy with a nudge after the mother moved on down the aisle.

"Didn't lose any gloves," the kid said. "Billy and Roscoe had cold hands, and I knew their mothers couldn't afford to get them any."

*Go on to the next page.*

© Steck-Vaughn Company

**111**

**Making Judgments**
**Unit Eight: Reading Comprehension**
Language Arts 4, SV 3890-5

Name _____  Date _____

✎  Answer each question about the story.

1. Do you think the woman should have scolded the boy? _____

   Explain your answer. _____

   _____


2. Do you think the writer should have said something to the woman? _____

   Explain your answer. _____

   _____


3. Do you think the boy should have kept his gloves? _____

   Explain your answer. _____

   _____


4. Should the boy have told his mother what happened to the gloves? _____

   Explain your answer. _____

   _____


5. Do you think the title *Cold Hands, Warm Heart* is a good one for this story?

   _____

   Explain your answer. _____

   _____

   _____

Name _____ Date _____

## It's How You Look At It

Betty's family moved into the house by the highway in the fall. The back of the house looked out over a little meadow between the house and a woods. Its trees grew on a steep hill that ran down to a creek. On the other side of the creek was another hill.

Betty became very interested in the lights she could see from a house on the far hill. At night it had many shining windows. As the leaves fell off the trees, she could see more of it; but she could not tell much about it. "It must be very grand," she thought. "It must be a much bigger house than our new home. I wonder who lives in such a grand house."

One evening Betty and her father got in the car and found the narrow road the other house was on. They had trouble deciding which house was the one Betty had seen. "None of the houses on this road looks so special up close," she said. Then all at once, she said, "This is the house. I know because I can see our house across the valley. But ours looks bigger from here."

The sun was setting, and it reflected off the windows of Betty's new house. "Look!" she cried. "Our house has golden windows!" On the way home she thought about the people who lived in the house she had seen. "They must look over at us and wonder who lives in the special house with the golden windows," she thought.

*Go on to the next page.*

Name _____ Date _____

## Summarizing, p. 2

 Write in your own words a summary of the story you read. Your summary should be three or four sentences long. Remember that a summary covers only the main points of a story and leaves out details that are less important.

Name _____  Date _____

## What Will Happen Next?

✎  Read each paragraph. Then answer the questions. Circle the letter in front of the correct answer.

Brian ran to get the mail as soon as he heard the mail truck drive away down the street. He looked through the bills, advertisements, and letters until he found the one that was addressed to him. He threw the rest of the mail on the table and ran up to his room. Brian quickly read the letter from his friend Mike. Then he went to his desk and got out a pen and some paper.

1. What will Brian do next?
   a. He will write a letter to his Aunt Sarah.
   b. He will send away for a free toy.
   c. He will do his homework.
   d. He will write a letter to his friend Mike.

Brian stamped his letter and ran to his bike. He rode downtown and mailed his letter at the post office. He wanted Mike to hear his news as soon as possible. That night, Brian heard that there was a problem with the mail. Some letters could be held up for several days. Brian went to talk to his mother, and then he went to the phone.

2. What will Brian do next?
   a. He will call the post office to see when his letter will get to Mike.
   b. He will call Mike and tell him the news that is in his letter.
   c. He will write Mike another letter to explain what is happening.
   d. He will get his letter back and deliver it himself.

*Go on to the next page.*

Name _____   Date _____

## What Will Happen Next?, p. 2

✐  Read each paragraph. Then answer the questions. Circle the letter in front of the correct answer.

Jane's mother dropped her off near the auditorium at her school. Jane went into the school and walked to her classroom. The other students were there putting on their costumes and makeup. Jane felt nervous as she put on her long dress. Jane and Patricia practiced their lines together, and then it was time to go backstage.

3.  What will the children do next?
   **a.**  They will watch a play.
   **b.**  They will go to a baseball game.
   **c.**  They will put on a play.
   **d.**  They will go home.

The audience clapped for a long time when the play was over. Everyone said it had been a wonderful performance. The actors were proud that everyone had remembered their lines. They all felt tired but excited and hungry, too. No one was ready to go home yet. Mrs. Donovan noted that the Pizza Palace was still open.

4.  What will the children do next?
   **a.**  They will go home and get some rest.
   **b.**  They will go to the Pizza Palace to eat.
   **c.**  They will go to Mrs. Donovan's house.
   **d.**  They will go to the Burger Barn to eat.

Name _____ Date _____

## What's the Main Idea?

✏️  Read each paragraph. Choose the answer that tells the main idea of each paragraph. Circle the letter in front of the correct answer.

Denzel had always wanted to go to Australia. He had heard about the open spaces and the ranches in the outback. He had read about the amazing wildlife that live in Australia's rainforests and deserts. He was always interested in learning more about Australia.

1. What is the main idea of this paragraph?
   **a.** Australia has open spaces and ranches.
   **b.** Australia has amazing wildlife.
   **c.** Denzel had always wanted to go to Australia.
   **d.** He was always interested in learning more about Australia.

One day Denzel found himself stepping off a plane in Australia. Denzel's dream of visiting Australia had come true. His family was taking a vacation there. Denzel took pictures of everything he saw, but he didn't think he would ever forget about any of it. Every day, Denzel saw something new and fascinating. He knew that someday he would visit Australia again.

2. What is the main idea of this paragraph?
   **a.** Denzel knew that he would visit Australia again.
   **b.** Every day, Denzel saw something new.
   **c.** Denzel took pictures of everything he saw.
   **d.** Denzel's dream of visiting Australia had come true.

*Go on to the next page.*

Name _____ Date _____

## What's the Main Idea?, p. 2

✐ Read each paragraph. Choose the answer that tells the main idea of each paragraph. Circle the letter in front of the correct answer.

Lin was very worried. She had not been able to sleep the night before, and now she did not have any appetite for breakfast. She went up to her room and paced the floor. She stared out of the window, frowning. Lin's research paper was due in just four days, and she was not prepared! No matter how hard she tried, she could not come up with a topic that she liked.

**3.** What is the main idea of this paragraph?
   **a.** Lin was very worried.
   **b.** She did not have any appetite for breakfast.
   **c.** Lin's research paper was due, and she was not prepared.
   **d.** Lin could not think of a topic that she liked.

At last, a thought struck Lin as she looked out the window. She sat down at her desk and began to write notes. She went to the library and did some research. She came back to her house and wrote some more. At dinnertime, Lin was very hungry. She cleaned her plate and went for seconds! Lin was no longer worried about her paper—she knew she had a great idea.

**4.** What is the main idea of this paragraph?
   **a.** At dinnertime, Lin was very hungry.
   **b.** Lin was no longer worried about her paper.
   **c.** She cleaned her plate and went for seconds.
   **d.** A thought struck Lin as she looked out the window.

Name _____ Date _____

## Finding the Main Idea

🖉  Read each paragraph. Then write the sentence from the paragraph that tells the main idea.

Mrs. Johnson always baked cakes for new people in her neighborhood. She listened to the children when they asked her questions and tried to help them if they had a problem. She always offered a helping hand if she knew that someone might need it. Mrs. Johnson was a very caring person.

**1.** What is the sentence that tells the main idea of this paragraph?

_____

_____

One day, the people in Mrs. Johnson's neighborhood found that she had become ill and had gone to the hospital. They wanted to show her how much they appreciated all she had done for them. Mrs. Johnson received many cards, gifts, and flowers while she was in the hospital. When she came home, she found her front steps covered with flowers, too. Someone had printed a huge banner welcoming her home, and there was a bouquet of bright balloons tied to her mailbox.

**2.** What is the sentence that tells the main idea of this paragraph?

_____

_____

*Go on to the next page.*

Name _____    Date _____

## Finding the Main Idea, p. 2

✎  Read each paragraph. Then write the sentence from the paragraph that tells the main idea.

Vacations can be fun and exciting, but they can be very tiring, too. When a person comes home from a vacation, there can be a lot of work to catch up on. There are suitcases to unpack and clothes to wash. At work, there can be papers piled on the desk that need immediate attention. There is so much to do. But the person who has just come back from a vacation feels too tired even to think about it!

**3.** What is the sentence that tells the main idea of this paragraph?

_____

_____

_____

If you plan well, you can avoid some of the stress of returning from vacation. Leave a couple of days at the end of vacation for resting at home. Sleep late in the morning if you want to. Get back into your normal routine slowly. Take time to think about your vacation. Get your pictures developed! Then you will be ready to go back to work or school.

**4.** What is the sentence that tells the main idea of this paragraph?

_____

_____

_____

Name _____    Date _____

## Say It Your Way

✐  Read each paragraph. Then write, in your own words, a sentence that tells what the paragraph is about.

Maureen could hardly believe she was going to be in fifth grade this year. She was very excited. But she was nervous, too. The fifth grade was in a different school. The students in her class would be the youngest  students in the school. She wondered if the older students would make fun of the younger ones. At the same time, Maureen thought it would be fun to be in a new school with older students. Her stomach was full of butterflies!

**1.** In your own words, what is this paragraph about?

_____

_____

_____

Maureen's first week of school answered many of her questions. Things were not the way she had thought they would be. The new school was large and full of interesting activities. The library was beautiful. The older students were in a different wing. Maureen did not see them often, but when she did, they always smiled at her. Maureen knew that being in the fifth grade was going to be even better than she had imagined.

**2.** In your own words, what is this paragraph about?

_____

_____

_____

*Go on to the next page.*

**Paraphrasing**
**Unit Eight: Reading Comprehension**
Language Arts 4, SV 3890-5

Name _____ Date _____

🖉 Read each paragraph. Then write, in your own words, a sentence that tells what the paragraph is about.

Greg was furious. A group of boys had invited Greg to go to the movies with them, but Greg's mother had said he couldn't go. She did not like the idea of boys his age going to a movie without an adult. Greg sat in his room all night and thought about how angry he was at his mother. He also thought about how embarrassed he would feel when he saw his friends again.

**3.** In your own words, what is this paragraph about?

_____

_____

_____

The next day, Greg found out that the boys who had gone to the movie had not had a very good time. One of them had begun a popcorn fight in the theater. People had complained, and the boys had to leave the movie. They had all gotten into trouble with their parents. Greg couldn't help feeling glad that he had not gone after all.

**4.** In your own words, what is this paragraph about?

_____

_____

_____

**Reality or Fantasy?**

# Drifting

Quinn was not sure how long he had been
drifting on the water. He had taken the little
sailboat out just after breakfast. His plan had been
to return in time for lunch, but he thought that he
had probably missed lunch by now. He couldn't
believe he had gotten stuck. He had been on this
water so many times he thought it would be easy to
go alone. But he didn't count on the wind dying
down. His eyes felt dry and sore, and he rubbed
them with his fists.

As he looked back out over the water, he began to see some odd things. He saw a
strange sea creature lift its head out of the water and watch him pass. A dolphin swam
by his boat calling, "Silly boy, silly boy!" His sail began speaking to him in a
whispery language. The waves slapped the boat and scolded him for being foolish
because he hadn't even told anyone where he was going. Suddenly, birds began to
scream at him and swoop down on him from the air. Their cries seemed angry, and
they knew his name!

Then Quinn opened his eyes. He sat up and looked around. He had heard his
name, but it was his brother calling, not some birds! He was there with the
powerboat, tying a line onto Quinn's little sailboat. Now Quinn would be towed in to
shore. Quinn didn't care if he did get into trouble; he was just glad to be going home!

*Go on to the next page.*

Name _____ Date _____

✐ Read each sentence about the story. Think whether the sentence is describing something real or something that is fantasy. Write *R* if the sentence tells about something that could really happen. Write *F* if the sentence tells about something that is fantasy and could not really happen.

1. Quinn had taken the little sailboat out just after breakfast. _____

2. His eyes felt dry and sore, and he rubbed them with his fists. _____

3. His sail began speaking to him in a whispery language. _____

4. His brother tied a line onto Quinn's little boat. _____

5. The waves scolded him for being foolish. _____

6. The birds screamed Quinn's name. _____

7. Quinn had not told anyone where he was going. _____

8. The wind had stopped blowing. _____

9. A dolphin swam by his boat calling, "Silly boy, silly boy!" _____

10. Quinn thought that he had probably missed lunch by now. _____

Name _____ Date _____

### Whose Hat Is That?

The hat had been given to Mrs. Beanwater many years before. It was the kind of pink that shows up a long way on a sunny day. It had a wide brim with little red cherries made of clay and a garden of tiny white flowers stuck in the band all around the brim.

The brim was a faded pink, even though the hat had always sat on a dark shelf. As soon as the friend who gave it to her left, Mrs. Beanwater sighed and said, "What a dreadful hat! What a frightfully ugly hat!"

The hat would still be on the shelf if it weren't for the crows. Mrs. Beanwater needed a hat for the scarecrow she made this summer. The friend who gave it to her had moved away, and Mrs. Beanwater was certain the hat would frighten anything that saw it.

As it turned out, the crows loved it; and so did Miss Dallywinkle. The crows sat along the brim picking at the clay cherries, and Miss Dallywinkle came to Mrs. Beanwater's door. "Since your scarecrow's lovely hat isn't working," Miss Dallywinkle said, "I wonder if you might swap it for a hat of mine that I'm certain will scare the crows."

No one ever found out. Starting the very next day the townspeople began admiring a black felt hat that Mrs. Beanwater wore from that day on; and the poor scarecrow, who wore it for less than an hour, has gone hatless ever since.

*Go on to the next page.*

Name _____ Date _____

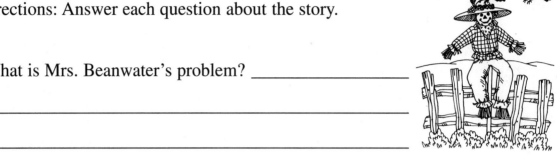

✏ Directions: Answer each question about the story.

1. What is Mrs. Beanwater's problem? _____

_____

_____

2. How does Mrs. Beanwater solve her problem?_____

_____

_____

3. What is Miss Dallywinkle's problem?_____

_____

_____

4. How does Miss Dallywinkle solve her problem? _____

_____

_____

5. How do the solutions in the story affect Mrs. Beanwater, the friend who

   gave her the pink hat, Miss Dallywinkle, and the scarecrow? _____

_____

_____

_____

_____

# Language Arts Handbook
## Grade Four
## Answer Key

P. 5    Unit One Assessment 1. proper noun, 2. common noun, 3. pronoun, 4. adjective, 5. present tense verb, 6. possessive noun, 7. contraction, 8. compound word, 9. plural noun, 10. past tense verb, 11. circle *is*, 12. circle *will*, 13. came, 14. went, 15. ate, 16. began, 17. thought, 18. said, 19. took, 20. grew, 21. found, 22. became

P. 6    1. <u>Eskimos</u> live in the coldest <u>places</u> in the <u>world</u>., 2. Many of them live in <u>Alaska</u>, the largest <u>state</u> in the <u>United States</u>., 3. Other <u>communities</u> are found in <u>Greenland</u> and <u>Canada</u>., 4. These <u>people</u> have adjusted to very bitter <u>temperatures</u>., 5. <u>Eskimos</u> who live in the <u>Arctic</u> hunt polar <u>bears</u>., 6. The <u>hunters</u> also track <u>walruses</u>., 7. These <u>animals</u> are valuable for their <u>meat</u> and for their <u>tusks</u> made of <u>ivory</u>., 8. This hard <u>material</u> is used to make <u>knives</u>, <u>hooks</u>, and other <u>tools</u>., 9. For <u>centuries</u> <u>Eskimos</u> have used <u>ice</u> from the <u>sea</u> for their fresh drinking <u>water</u>., 10. They speak a <u>language</u> that is different from the <u>speech</u> of other <u>American Indians</u>., 11. Many <u>Eskimos</u> once lived in special <u>homes</u>., 12. These <u>buildings</u> are called <u>igloos</u>.

P. 7    1. students, 2. graders, 3. ones, 4. birthday, 5. puppy, 6. guests, 7. scarf, 8. cards, gifts, 9. bedspread, 10. curtains

P. 8    1. huskies, 2. feet, 3. axes, 4. lives, 5. walruses, 6. caribou, reindeer, 7. tools, 8. women

P. 9    1. Mary loved listening to her grandfather's stories., 2. Mary and her mother saw their neighbors' snow machines., 3. All the family's friends came to the birthday party., 4. Mary opened the relatives' presents., 5. She read her birthday cards, and some of the cards' messages were funny., 6. James' present was a surprise., 7. Mary's heart was full of love.

P. 10    1. Mike's, 2. car's, 3. Dan's, 4. dad's, 5. neighbors', 6. people's, 7. pet's, 8. children's, 9. neighbors', 10. store's, 11. brother's

P. 11    1. carved, 2. climbed, 3. talked, 4. shivered, 5. stuffed, 6. added, 7. propped, 8. flashed, 9. surprised, 10. knocked, 11. yelled, 12. laughed

P. 12    1. will work, 2. hope, 3. needed, 4. banged, 5. play

P. 13    1. drummed, 2. listened, cheered, 3. cried, 4. hurried, 5. waved, 6. wailed, 7. watched, 8. trotted, ended

P. 14    1. <u>were</u>, 2. <u>were dying</u>, 3. <u>had given</u>, 4. <u>were hoping</u>, 5. <u>had fallen</u>, 6. <u>was soaking</u>

Pp. 15–16    1. come, 2. began, 3. sang, 4. become, 5. built, 6. given, 7. made, 8. found, 9. led, 10. found, 11. written, 12. took, 13. began, 14. went

P. 17    Answers may vary. 1. A, poor, 2. a, kind, 3. injured, own, 4. the, hurt, 5. a, soft, 6. strong, 7. good

P. 18    1. most unusual, 2. more interested, 3. duller, 4. most exciting, 5. most beautiful, 6. fastest, 7. more graceful, 8. most thrilling

P. 19    1. loneliest, 2. sadder, 3. longer, 4. luckier, 5. prettiest, 6. lighter, 7. happiest, 8. greatest

P. 20    1. busily, 2. desperately, 3. carefully, 4. wearily, 5. quietly, 6. Finally, 7. happily, 8 loudly, here, 9. proudly

P. 21    1. He, 2. She, 3. him, 4. Their, 5. my

P. 22    (Answers may vary.) 1. me, 2. them, 3. you, 4. it, 5. it, 6. me, or us, 7. it, 8. it, 9. us, 10., it, 11. it, 12. us

P. 23    1. Yellow/hammer, 2. Sun/shine, 3. Sun/flower, 4. Corn/husker, 5. Ever/green

P. 24    1. We're, 2. You're, isn't, 3. that's, 4. How's, 5. We'll, they're 6. can't, 7. wouldn't, You'll, 8. You've, 9. haven't, aren't 10. they'll, they've, 11. it'll, 12. we've, who's, 13. Let's, 14. don't

P. 25    Unit Two Assessment: 1-2, answers will vary. Examples: 1. goes to camp every summer; circle *goes to camp.*, underline *family,* 2. My grandfather; circle *loves* underline *grandfather,* 3. exclamatory, 4. interrogative, 5. declarative, 6. imperative, 7. The prince and the king live in the palace., 8. Cindi's doll has brown hair and is wearing skates., 9. Raoul loved to draw, and he made pictures of many animals., 10. He was feeling lonely, sad, and tired., 11-14. Answers will vary. Examples: 11. wild, brown, fast, 12. white, beautiful, 13. wise, 14. hungry, quickly

P. 26    Subjects and predicates will vary. Possible responses: 1. helps you remember things, 2. A test, 3. Social studies, 4. is the way we communicate, 5. tells a complete thought

P. 27    1. interrogative, ?, 2. declarative, ., 3. declarative, ., 4. imperative, 5. interrogative, ?, 6. declarative, ., 7. exclamatory, !, 8. imperative, ., 9. declarative, ., 10. exclamatory, !

P. 28    Answers will vary. Example: The king wanted to find his son and offered a reward. Strong men and wise men searched for the prince. One boy knew the secret places of the forest and decided to look for the prince. He found the prince in a cave and figured out how to free him. The prince and the boy ran all the way to the palace.

P. 29    You'll never guess what happened today! My pig escaped from the barn. Have I sent you his picture? He is only two months old. He is cute, pink, and tiny. Mr. Carter caught him and gave him milk. The milk was sweet and warm. My poor pig was so scared, tired, and hungry. I'm so happy that he's safe.

P. 30    1. Do you like to draw, or do you like to paint?, 2. I can draw with crayons, or I can draw with pencils., 3. I'd like to paint now, but I'll make a mess., 4. I like old paintings, and I like color photographs., 5. I will take a drawing class, or I might take a painting class., 6. Right now I'm drawing, but I'd rather paint.

P. 31    Answers will vary. Examples: 1. carved, 2. searched, 3. climbed, 4. peered, 5. raced, 6. yelled, 7. fell, 8. cheered

P. 32    Answers will vary., 1. wise, 2. yellow, 3. grizzly, 4. bravely, 5. fierce, 6. adorable, 7. cuddly, 8. white

P. 33    Unit Three Assessment: 1. angry, 2. grew, 3. beautiful, 4. silly, 5. finish, 6. usually, 7. <u>art</u>ist, 8. <u>un</u>lucky, 9. taste<u>less</u>, 10. <u>im</u>possible, 11. flex<u>ible</u>, 12. patient<u>ly</u>, 13. <u>re</u>do, 14. <u>in</u>active, 15. hope<u>ful</u>, 16. too, 17. eye, 18. eight, 19. I, 20. me, 21. enjoy, 22. looks, 23. your, 24. There, here, 25. I

P. 34    Answers will vary. Possible answers: 1. horrible, 2. fierce, 3. chief, 4. discover, 5. brave, 6. begged, 7. explained, 8. surprising, 9. fighting, 10. peaceful, 11. happy, 12. disaster

P. 35    Answers will vary. Possible answers: 1. hot, tiny, 2. nervous, 3. push, 4. cried, 5. many, 6. big, funny, 7. Quickly, 8. stopped, 9. never, 10. true

P. 36    1. unfair, 2. impatiently, 3. preplanned, 4. misunderstood, 5. uncovered, 6. retraced, 7. distrusted, 8. incapable

P. 37    1. stormy, 2. visitor, 3. homeless, 4. politely, 5. musical, 6. wonderful, 7. magical, 8. remarkable, 9. friendly, 10. delightful

P. 38    Sentences will vary. Definitions: 1. sad, gloomy, depressed, 2. passes quickly, 3. a list of related numbers arranged in an orderly way for reference, 4. a round of applause

P. 39    1. meets, 2. read, 3. Would, 4. choose, 5. hear, 6. pale, 7. knew, 8. tail, 9. wait, 10. heard

P. 40    1. Dr., 2. Dr., 3. Sat., 4. Mr., Ave., 5. St., 6. Jan.

P. 41    1. You're, 2. your, 3. Your, 4. too, 5. to, 6. two, 7. too, 8. you're, 9. Your, 10. Your, too, 11. too, 12. your, 13. you're, 14. your, 15. too

P. 42    1. their, 2. They're, 3. There, 4. They're, 5. they're, 6. their, 7. there, 8. their, 9. There, 10. there, 11. their, 12. They're, there

P. 43    1. good, 2. good, 3. good, 4. good, 5. good, 6. good, 7. well, 8. good, 9. well, 10. good, 11. good, 12. Good, 13. well, 14. good

P. 44    1. I, 2. I, 3. me, 4. I, 5. I, 6. me, 7. I, 8. I, 9. me, 10. me, 11. me, 12. I, 13. I, 14. me, 15. me, 16. me, 17. me, 18. I

P. 45    1. its, 2. It's, 3. its, 4. it's, 5. its, 6. it's, 7. its, 8. It's, 9. it's, 10. its B. <u>It's</u> a fact that animals do not kill each other for fun. For example, one animal might attack another in order to feed <u>its</u> family. Because every animal has <u>its</u> enemies, each one has <u>its</u> own way to defend <u>its</u> life, <u>its</u> home, and <u>its</u> young.

P. 46    1. blows, 2. is, 3. promises, 4. looks, 5. discovers, 6. put, 7. say, 8. refuses, 9. escape, 10. earns, 11. proves, 12. enjoy

P. 47    Unit Four Assessment: 1. "That was a great play," said Susan., 2. Mrs. Beasley is the only person who didn't come., 3. Larry likes the way his car looks now., 4. Does class begin at 3:00 P.M. or 2:30 P.M.?, 5. What a horrible ending!, 6. Have you read the book

---

© Steck-Vaughn Company

**127**

Language Arts 4, SV 3890-5

The Long Trail Home?, 7. I wrote a poem called "Frost on the Windows.", 8. School has been fun this year., 9. We went on a field trip to Boston, Massachusetts., 10. We went on May 4, 1999, 11. Susan says that the best holiday is Thanksgiving Day., 12. That is the last time I will give Joe Carmel a ride in my car!, 13. Dr. Jones was the last one here, and he left at 3:15 A.M., 14. Tell me if you like the book Gone With the Wind.

P. 48   1. School started last week., 2. This year I have a new teacher., 3. Her name is Ms. Aarvig., 4. She has given us some interesting arithmetic problems., 5. Some of the problems were even funny., 6. We had to figure out some strange things., 7. The problems took a long time to solve, 8. Our group was the first one finished., 9. The answers we got were really amazing., 10. One of my favorite books is The Amazing Number Machine., 11. My brother is reading the story "The Math Magician.", 12. My teacher read aloud the article "It All Adds Up.", 13. Have you ever read the poem "Crazy Eights"?

P. 49   1. Sherman Smith has an unusual nickname., 2. His nickname is Sherlock Shoe., 3. Someone took Cindi's doll., 4. The only suspect is Tony Treworgy., 5. Dr. Wesley does not have the doll., 6. Dr. Carter treated a boy the same morning., 7. Mrs. Smith told Sherlock to ask Capt. Kent for help., 8. Did you see where I left my doll?, 9. I cannot believe that I lost it., 10. I am going to Tony Treworgy's house., 11. I know I left my doll in the waiting room., 12. How will I solve this mystery?

P. 50   1. I am proud that Alaska is the largest state., 2. Alaska's eastern neighbor is Canada., 3. The state capital of Alaska is Juneau., 4. I have visited Mt. McKinley with my father., 5. I would like to visit the Aleutian Islands., 6. My father tells stories about the copper mines at Kennicott., 7. He once mined gold along the Stikine River., 8. My father fishes along the Yukon River., 9. He also likes to visit Anchorage., 10. I live on Nyac Street., 11. The grocery store is at the corner of Blizzard Avenue., 12. The dogsled flies along Husky Boulevard., 13. My grandmother lives on Harpoon Lane., 14. Elk Circle is the location of my new school.

P. 51   1. The boys arrived in Philadelphia on Thursday, 2. Friday morning they found their father., 3. All day Saturday they slept., 4. They celebrated John's birthday on Sunday., 5. Their journey started in July., 6. It was during August when they reached Philadelphia., 7. In September the boys started school, 8. They received a message from their mother October 2., 9. She would join them on Halloween., 10. The entire family would be together on Thanksgiving., 11. They would celebrate Christmas together., 12. The boys planned to show their mother on New Year's Day that they could read.

P. 52   1. The new arithmetic books are red and yellow., 2. Arithmetic is my first class every morning., 3. Pages full of arithmetic problems are a challenge., 4. Mr. Washington is my arithmetic teacher this year., 5. Class starts every day at 8:15 A.M., 6. Sometimes Dr. Pritchett attends our class., 7. Sally N. Right is the smartest girl in my arithmetic class., 8. T. C. Russell won an award at the arithmetic fair., 9. I shared my book today with J. D. Kline., 10. I. Arithmetic Every Day, A. In the classroom, B. At home, C. At the store

P. 53   1. ?, 2. !, 3. ?, 4. !, 5. !, 6. ?, 7. !, 8. !, 9. ?, 10. !, 11. ?, 12. !, 13. ?, 14. ?, 15. !, 16. ?, 17. ?, 18. !

P. 54   1. 45 Harper Road/Icetown, Alaska 99682/November 15, 1999, 2. 8260 Polar Lane/Winter Park, Florida 32792/August 2, 1999, 3. 94 Klondike Circle/Juneau, Alaska 99673/December 23, 1999, 4. 69 Tundra Avenue/Yonkers, New York 10710/June 27, 1999, 5. Dear Aunt Rita, 6. Sincerely yours, 7. Dear Mother, 8. Your friend, 9. Dear Apah, 10. Your sister, 11. Dear Mika, 12. Love,

P. 55   1. Yes, Mrs. and Mrs. Saxby helped the boys., 2. First, he told them about the plan. 3. The boys studied letters, words, and maps., 4. Mrs. Saxby talked about Searsville, Richmond, Washington, and Philadelphia. 5. Mr. Saxby had a map, but the

boys lost the map., 6. Mrs. Saxby pasted a label on a jar, and she put jelly in it., 7. Andy, you must pretend that this is not yours., 8. "Travel by day," said Mr. Saxby.

P. 56   1. Erika's birthday was on a cold winter day., 2. The children's faces lit up when they saw the snow., 3. The two girls' walk home was difficult., 4. Her mother's voice greeted Erika., 5. "We don't have everything for your party.", 6. "I'll go to the store," Erika replied., 7. "Where's father?" Erika asked., 8. "We'll look for your father on the way to the store.", 9. She added, "Father left at 6:30 this morning.", 10. "I left school at 1:15 this afternoon," said Erika.

P. 57   1. "Dad is bringing home a puppy today," Trudi said., 2. "What kind of puppy will he choose?" asked Donald., 3. Truly said, "I asked for a pug.", 4. "Where is my puppy?" Trudi asked., 5. "Go into the yard, Trudi," her mother replied., 6. "Is it in the yard?" Trudi asked eagerly., 7. Trudi wrote a poem called "My Puppy.", 8. She read a story called "Our Dog Dan.", 9. Trudi read the book How to Be a Good Master., 10. Then she watched the television show Lassie., 11. She read The Alphabet Book to her baby brother., 12. Next, she will read A Trip to the Zoo to him.

P.58   Unit Five Assessment: Writing will vary. Students should write complete sentences, well written paragraphs, and follow other requirements of writing type chosen.

P.59   Characters: Teresa, friends, Setting: Teresa's house, living room, Problem: lights go out, do not come back on in living room, Conclusion: Teresa lights candles and saves party

P. 60   Conversations will vary. Check for quotation marks and correct punctuation.

P. 61   Answers will vary. Possible answers: A jack-o-lantern's jolly smile/Glowed like a lamp in the lonely night/Till an owl flew by with a spooky cry/And the howling wind blew out the light

P. 62   Answers will vary. Students should think of a workable solution to the problem, use dialogue and stage directions.

P. 63   Who?: John Henry, What?: raced against steam drill and won, When?: today, 11:30 A.M., Where?: West Virginia, Why?: to prove that he was fastest and strongest steel driver

P. 64   Answers will vary. Possible responses: 1. What ingredients are in Italian Minestrone?, 2. What is your favorite soup?, 3. What is the most unusual soup you make?

P. 65   I danced with the prince until midnight. I heard the clock chime and ran home. The prince looked for me. He tried my shoe on every girl in the kingdom. Finally, the prince found me. We were married and lived happily ever after.

P. 66   Possible answers: 2, 4. Sentence 2 answers question that Benjy asked Jason., Sentence 4 responds to the news in Benjy's letter.

P. 67   1. Mr. Cravitz, 2. lunch, 3. Mr. and Mrs. Bunker's house, Saturday, June 2, 4. 1 P.M., 4 P.M.

P. 68   Answers will vary.

P. 69   Addresses will vary, but should follow correct form as shown.

P. 70   Journal entries will vary, but should include date and some details about what happened and how student felt.

P. 71   1. a collection of tales from Africa, 2. Harold Courlander, 3. because he or she likes the humor in it

P. 72   Unit Six Assessment: Answers will vary. Paragraph should relate to picture and use rules for a good paragraph. Students' paragraphs should be good example of type chosen.

P. 73   Possible responses: 1. You can go swimming., 2. The days are longer., 3. There is no school.

P. 74   Correct order, 2, 4, 6, 1, 3, 5

P. 75   1. Subjects-both fall asleep under spell, 2. Magic-poisoned apple, magic fog, 3. Ending-live happily ever after

P. 76   1. Boy smarter than witches; left trail, hid boat, and did not look into their eyes

P. 77   Cause: Dog was hungry, Effect: Began walking, Got lost, Effect: Used nose to get home, Effect: boy was happy and gave dog a bone

P. 78   Possible responses for 3: Word: responsibility; web words: